# Target
## Get back on track

# Pearson Edexcel GCSE (9–1)
# Chemistry

## Nora Henry, Helen Sayers and Dorothy Warren

Pearson

C000109101

Published by Pearson Education Limited, 80 Strand, London, WC2R 0RL.

www.pearsonschoolsandfecolleges.co.uk

Copies of official specifications for all Pearson qualifications may be found on the website: qualifications.pearson.com

Text and illustrations © Pearson Education Ltd 2018
Typeset and illustrated by QBS Learning
Produced by QBS Learning

The rights of Nora Henry, Helen Sayers and Dorothy Warren to be identified as authors of this work have been asserted by them in accordance with the Copyright, Designs and Patents Act 1988.

First published 2018

21 20 19 18
10 9 8 7 6 5 4 3 2 1

**British Library Cataloguing in Publication Data**
A catalogue record for this book is available from the British Library

ISBN 978 1 292 24580 5

**Copyright notice**
All rights reserved. No part of this publication may be reproduced in any form or by any means (including photocopying or storing it in any medium by electronic means and whether or not transiently or incidentally to some other use of this publication) without the written permission of the copyright owner, except in accordance with the provisions of the Copyright, Designs and Patents Act 1988 or under the terms of a licence issued by the Copyright Licensing Agency, Barnard's Inn, 86 Fetter Lane, London EC4A 1EN (www.cla.co.uk). Applications for the copyright owner's written permission should be addressed to the publisher.

Printed in Slovakia by Neografia

**Note from the publisher**
1. While the publishers have made every attempt to ensure that advice on the qualifications and its assessment is accurate, the official specification and associated guidance materials are the only authoritative source of information and should always be referred to for definitive guidance. Pearson examiners have not contributed to any sections in this resource relevant to examination papers for which they have responsibility.
2. Pearson has robust editorial processes, including answer and fact checks, to ensure the accuracy of the content in this publication, and every effort is made to ensure this publication is free of errors. We are, however, only human, and occasionally errors do occur. Pearson is not liable for any misunderstandings that arise as a result of errors in this publication, but it is our priority to ensure that the content is accurate. If you spot an error, please do contact us at resourcescorrections@pearson.com so we can make sure it is corrected.

---

This workbook has been developed using the Pearson Progression Map and Scale for Science.

To find out more about the Progression Scale for Science and to see how it relates to indicative GCSE (9–1) grades go to www.pearsonschools.co.uk/ProgressionServices

## Helping you to formulate grade predictions, apply interventions and track progress.

Any reference to indicative grades in the Pearson Target Workbooks and Pearson Progression Services is not to be used as an accurate indicator of how a student will be awarded a grade for their GCSE exams.

You have told us that mapping the Steps from the Pearson Progression Maps to indicative grades will make it simpler for you to accumulate the evidence to formulate your own grade predictions, apply any interventions and track student progress. We're really excited about this work and its potential for helping teachers and students. It is, however, important to understand that this mapping is for guidance only to support teachers' own predictions of progress and is not an accurate predictor of grades.

Our Pearson Progression Scale is criterion referenced. If a student can perform a task or demonstrate a skill, we say they are working at a certain Step according to the criteria. Teachers can mark assessments and issue results with reference to these criteria which do not depend on the wider cohort in any given year. For GCSE exams however, all Awarding Organisations set the grade boundaries with reference to the strength of the cohort in any given year. For more information about how this works please visit: https://qualifications.pearson.com/en/support/support-topics/results-certification/understanding-marks-and-grades.html/Teacher

# Contents

# ① Moles

This unit will help you to describe what a mole is and how to do calculations involving moles. It will also help you calculate an empirical formula.

In the exam, you will be asked to answer questions such as the one below.

**Exam-style question**

1   Calcium carbonate, $CaCO_3$, decomposes to form calcium oxide and carbon dioxide when it is heated.

   (a)   Calculate the number of moles in 286 g of $CaCO_3$.

   (relative atomic masses: Ca = 40, C = 12, O = 16)

   number of moles = ..................................................                    **(2 marks)**

   (b)   Calculate the number of molecules in 5 mol of carbon dioxide.

   number of molecules = ..................................................                **(1 mark)**

   (c)   A sample of calcium oxide contains 50 g of calcium and 20 g of oxygen by mass. Calculate the empirical formula of calcium oxide.

   empirical formula = ..................................................                   **(3 marks)**

You will already have done some work on moles. Before starting the **skills boosts**, rate your confidence in each area. Colour in 🖉 the bars.

① **How do I describe what a mole is?**

② **How do I calculate how many moles, or particles, there are in a substance?**

③ **How do I calculate empirical formulae?**

Moles are a way to consider the proportions, or ratios, of different substances involved in a reaction. A balanced equation for a reaction shows that the proportions of the substances in moles will always be the same. The SI unit symbol for the mole is mol.

You will have learned that potential difference is measured in volts using the symbol V (e.g. a potential difference of three volts is 3 V). Similarly, the amount of substance is measured in moles using the symbol mol (e.g. an amount of substance of three moles is 3 mol). Use the unit 'mol' when a number is involved. For example, 1 mol of propane reacts with 5 mol of oxygen to produce 3 mol of carbon dioxide and 4 mol of water.

> **Remember** Do not confuse the quantity **mole** with the particle **molecule**.

**(1)** Complete ✐ the equation.                    Look at the text above to help you.

$$C_3H_8 + \text{............} O_2 \rightarrow \text{............} CO_2 + \text{............} H_2O$$

Moles are also a way to consider the proportions of different particles within a substance.
For example:
   1 mol of methane molecules, $CH_4$, contains 5 mol of atoms (1 mol of C atoms, 4 mol of H atoms).
   1 mol of the ionic compound sodium chloride, NaCl, contains 1 mol of $Na^+$ ions and 1 mol of $Cl^-$ ions.

**(2)** Draw ✐ lines to join each particle to the number of moles of that particle contained in 1 mol of calcium hydroxide, $Ca(OH)_2$. More than one particle may link to a number.

| Particle | | Number of moles |
|---|---|---|
| H atoms | | 1 |
| $Ca^{2+}$ ions | | 2 |
| $OH^-$ ions | | 3 |
| O atoms | | 4 |

**(3)** Write ✐ the number of moles of the different particles in 1 mol of ammonium hydroxide, $NH_4OH$.

.................................................................................................

.................................................................................................

> In this formula, there are atoms and ions. Write down all the atoms and ions and how many there are of each.

**(4)** Complete ✐ the sentence below for this equation:

$$Cu^{2+} + 2e^- \rightarrow Cu$$

This reaction has ............ mol of $Cu^{2+}$ ions, ............ mol of electrons and ............ mol of Cu atoms.

You need to use the following when answering some questions.
- The relative atomic mass ($A_r$) for an atom is given in the periodic table. It is the average mass of 1 mol of atoms of that element.
- The relative formula mass ($M_r$) of an ionic compound, molecule or giant covalent substance is the sum of the relative atomic masses of the atoms in the formula.

> **Remember** A giant covalent substance can be an element, for example, diamond or graphite (which are forms of carbon). It can also be a compound, such as silica (which contains silicon and oxygen atoms).

# 1    How do I describe what a mole is?

You need to recall the definition of a mole and use it to describe quantities of substances.

One **mole** of particles of a substance is defined as either:

- the Avogadro constant number of particles ($6.02 \times 10^{23}$ atoms, molecules, formulae or ions)

or:

- a mass of relative particle mass g.

For example, each mole of methane, $CH_4$, contains $6.02 \times 10^{23}$ $CH_4$ molecules.

In this definition, 'particles' covers atoms, ions, electrons, molecules and compounds.

**(1)** Circle Ⓐ the $A_r$ for lithium.

```
┌─────────────┐
│      7      │
│     Li      │
│      3      │
└─────────────┘
```

If you are not given the $A_r$ values, you can find them in the periodic table.

**(2)** Complete 🖊 these sentences.

> The relative particle mass could be:
>
> - the relative ............................................... mass, ..............................................., found in the
>
>   ............................................... table
>
> - the ..............................................., $M_r$, calculated from ............................... values and the chemical formula.

**(3)** Calculate 🖊 the relative particle mass of a sulfur dioxide molecule, $SO_2$.

$A_r$ for sulfur, S, is 32

$A_r$ for oxygen, O, is 16

**Remember** $SO_2$ has two oxygen atoms.

The relative particle mass of $SO_2$ is ............ + ............ + ............ = ............

So 1 mol of $SO_2$ molecules has a mass of ............................... g

If there is a 2 outside the brackets it means there is 2 times everything inside the brackets.

**(4)** Complete 🖊 the table. Use a periodic table to help you.

| Substance | Particle type | Formula | Relative particle mass | Mass of 1 mol (g) |
|---|---|---|---|---|
| Sodium chloride | ions | NaCl | 23 + 35.5 = 58.5 | 58.5 |
| Magnesium chloride | | | | |
| Water | | | | |
| Glucose | | $C_6H_{12}O_6$ | | |
| Sulfate | ion | $SO_4^{2-}$ | | |
| | | $Ca(NO_3)_2$ | | |

**Remember** We can also have moles of electrons.

## ② How do I calculate how many moles, or particles, there are in a substance?

You can calculate the **number of moles** in a substance if you know the mass of the substance. If you know the number of moles, you can calculate how many particles there are using the Avogadro constant.

You can use this equation to calculate the number of moles in a certain mass of a substance:

$$\text{number of moles} = \frac{\text{mass of substance (g)}}{A_r \text{ or } M_r}$$

**Exam-style question**

1   Calculate the number of moles in 185.25 g of $CuCO_3$.

(relative atomic masses: Cu = 63.5, C = 12, O = 16)

① **a** Circle Ⓐ the value for mass in the question.

**b** The $M_r$ of $CuCO_3$ is 123.5. Show 🖉 how this is calculated.

.............................................................................................................................................................................

.............................................................................................................................................................................

**c** Substitute the values into the equation and calculate 🖉 the answer.

$$\text{number of moles} = \frac{\text{mass (g)}}{M_r} = \frac{\boxed{\phantom{xxxxx}}}{\boxed{\phantom{xxxxx}}} = \text{..................... mol}$$

**Exam-style question**

2   Calculate the number of moles of chlorine molecules in 213 g of chlorine.

(relative formula mass: $Cl_2 = 71$)

② **a** Highlight 🖉 the values in the question.

**b** Calculate 🖉 the answer. $\text{number of moles} = \dfrac{\boxed{\phantom{xxx}}}{\boxed{\phantom{xxx}}} = \text{.............................}$

To calculate the **number of particles** in a substance, multiply the number of moles by the Avogadro constant. (Avogadro constant = $6.02 \times 10^{23}$ per mole)

> **Remember** 1 mol of particles of a substance contains $6.02 \times 10^{23}$ particles.

③ Use your answer to ② to calculate 🖉 the number of molecules in 213 g of chlorine.

........................................................................................................

.............................. molecules

> The Avogadro constant and the mass are given to 3 significant figures (sf), so calculate your answers to 3 sf too.

> Make sure you know how to enter numbers in standard form in your calculator.

④ Calculate 🖉 the mass of 0.06 mol of ammonia, $NH_3$.
(relative formula mass of ammonia, $NH_3 = 17$)

> Rearrange the equation to make mass the subject.

## 3 How do I calculate empirical formulae?

An empirical formula is the simplest whole number ratio of atoms or ions in a substance. It can be calculated from the masses of the elements it contains.

Read the exam-style questions, and answer them by following the questions below.

**Remember** Use a periodic table to find the $A_r$ values you need.

### Exam-style question

1   224 g of iron reacts with 96 g of oxygen.
    Calculate the empirical formula of the iron oxide made.

① **a** Circle (A) the mass of iron used.

**b** What is the $A_r$ of oxygen? (✏) ...............................................................................

**c** Complete (✏) the table.

| | Iron (Fe) | Oxygen (O) |
|---|---|---|
| Mass (g) | | 96 |
| Relative atomic mass, $A_r$ | 56 | |
| $\dfrac{\text{mass}}{A_r}$ = number of moles | $\dfrac{\boxed{\phantom{00}}}{56} = 4$ | $\dfrac{96}{\boxed{\phantom{00}}} = 6$ |
| Find the simplest ratio of the number of moles. Divide by the smallest number | $\dfrac{4}{4} = 1$ | $\dfrac{6}{4} = 1.5$ |
| If needed, multiply by 2 to make the simplest ratio as whole numbers | 2 | 3 |
| Ratio of atoms | ............... iron atoms for every ............... oxygen atoms | |
| Empirical formula | $Fe_2O_3$ | |

You do not have to set your working out in a table, but it is good practice to lay it out in separate columns for each element.

You cannot have half an atom, so you need to check that **both** the highlighted numbers are whole numbers.

**Remember** Write down the empirical formula when you have done your calculation.

### Exam-style question

2   5.4 g of aluminium reacts with 21.3 g of chlorine.
    Calculate the empirical formula of the aluminium chloride made.

② **a** Circle (A) the masses in the question.

**b** Where will you find the values for $A_r$? (✏) ...............................................................................

**c** On paper, complete (✏) the calculation by writing out a table like the one above.

# Sample response

Use these sample responses to questions about moles to see some common errors made in these types of questions. Look back at the skills boosts to help you.

**Exam-style question**

1   Calculate the number of moles in 69 g of sodium carbonate, $Na_2CO_3$.

(relative atomic masses: Na = 23, C = 12, O = 16)

The student gave the following answer. An appropriate number of significant figures has been used.

$M_r = 23 + 12 + 16 = 51$

$$\text{number of moles} = \frac{mass}{M_r}$$

$$= \frac{69}{51} = 1.3529 = 1.4 \, mol$$

**Remember** $M_r$ is the sum of the relative atomic masses of all the atoms or ions in the formula.

① **a**   Look at the student answer and highlight ✏ the parts that are correct.

**b**   Circle Ⓐ the parts that are wrong.

**c**   Write ✏ the answer.

When answering this type of question, work out the $M_r$ first, then substitute the numbers into the equation:

$$\text{number of moles} = \frac{mass}{M_r}$$

**Exam-style question**

2   A sample of lead bromide contains 41.4 g of lead and 32 g of bromine by mass. Calculate the empirical formula of lead bromide.

(relative atomic masses: Pb = 207, Br = 80)

② **a**   One student's answer is shown in the table on the left. Circle Ⓐ the mistakes the student has made.

**b**   Complete ✏ the table on the right to show the correct calculation.

The Avogadro constant is the number of particles found in a mole of any substance. Remember that in this definition, 'particles' means atoms, ions, electrons, molecules and compounds.

| Lead (Pb) | Bromine (Br) |
|---|---|
| $\frac{32}{270} = 0.12$ | $\frac{41.4}{80} = 0.52$ |
| $\frac{0.12}{0.12} = 1$ | $\frac{0.52}{0.12} = 4.3$ |
| Empirical formula is $PbBr_4$ | |

| Lead (Pb) | Bromine (Br) |
|---|---|
| | |
| | |
| | |

Empirical formula is ...................................

# Your turn!

It is now time to use what you have learned to answer the exam-style question from page 1. Remember to read the question thoroughly, looking for information that may help you. Make good use of your knowledge from other areas of chemistry.

## Exam-style question

1   Calcium carbonate, $CaCO_3$, decomposes to form calcium oxide and carbon dioxide when it is heated.

(a)   Calculate the number of moles in 286 g of $CaCO_3$.

Which equation do you need to use?

(relative atomic masses: Ca = 40, C = 12, O = 16)

What do you need to calculate first?

**(2 marks)**

number of moles = ......................................

(b)   Calculate the number of molecules in 5 mol of carbon dioxide.

Avogadro constant = $6.02 \times 10^{23}$ mol$^{-1}$

**(1 mark)**

number of molecules = ......................................

(c)   A sample of calcium oxide contains 50 g of calcium and 20 g of oxygen by mass.

Calculate the empirical formula of calcium oxide.

**Remember** It helps to set out separate columns for each element.

**(3 marks)**

empirical formula = ......................................

# Need more practice?

Questions about moles and empirical formulae could occur as part of a question on most chemistry topics, usually as a calculation, or as part of a question about an experiment or investigation.

Have a go at these exam-style questions.

**Exam-style questions**

1   Calculate the number of moles of lithium ions in 282 g of lithium sulfate, $Li_2SO_4$.

(relative atomic masses: Li = 7, S = 32, O = 16)                         **(3 marks)**

number of moles of lithium ions = .................................

2   Calculate the number of hydroxide ions in 0.5 mol of sodium hydroxide, NaOH.      **(1 mark)**

number of ions = .................................

3   A compound contains 360 g of carbon, 60 g of hydrogen and 1065 g of chlorine by mass. Calculate the empirical formula of this compound.

(relative atomic masses: C = 12, H = 1, Cl = 35.5)                         **(3 marks)**

empirical formula = .................................

**Boost your grade**

Practise making up your own calculations. Include compounds with more-challenging formulae.

How confident do you feel about each of these **skills**? Colour in  the bars.

**1** How do I describe what a mole is?

**2** How do I calculate how many moles, or particles, there are in a substance?

**3** How do I calculate empirical formulae?

# (2) Chemistry calculations

This unit will help you to set out different chemistry calculations clearly and give your answers to an appropriate number of significant figures.

In the exam, you will be asked to answer questions such as the one below.

**Exam-style question**

1   Ammonium sulfate is a salt used as a fertiliser.

Ammonia solution reacts with dilute sulfuric acid to produce ammonium sulfate.

$$2NH_3(aq) + H_2SO_4(aq) \rightarrow (NH_4)_2SO_4(aq)$$

(a)   Calculate the relative formula mass of sulfuric acid.

(relative atomic masses: N = 14, H = 1, O = 16, S = 32)

relative formula mass = ................................................   (1 mark)

(b)   Calculate the mass of ammonium sulfate produced when 3.4 g of ammonia reacts with excess sulfuric acid.

Give your answer to two significant figures.

mass = ................................................ g   (3 marks)

You will already have done some work on chemistry calculations. Before starting the **skills boosts**, rate your confidence in each area. Colour in ✏️ the bars.

**①** How do I set out calculations in a logical step-by-step way?

**②** How do I give answers to an appropriate number of significant figures?

**③** How do I calculate the mass of a reactant or product?

'Calculate' means obtain a numerical answer, showing relevant working and including any units. Sometimes you will use an equation to calculate a numerical answer. The best approach is to answer the question in a systematic and organised way, showing your method step by step. You can obtain marks for showing your understanding, even if you get the wrong answer.

Here is an example of an equation:

$$\text{number of moles} = \frac{\text{mass of substance (g)}}{A_r \text{ or } M_r}$$

$A_r$ is the abbreviation for relative atomic mass and $M_r$ is the abbreviation for relative formula mass.

If you know the number of moles and want to find the mass, you need to rearrange the equation.

---

To rearrange equations of the type $A = \dfrac{B}{C}$

**Make B the subject**

Multiply both sides by C: $A \times C = B \times \dfrac{\cancel{C}}{\cancel{C}}$

C cancels out on the right-hand side:

$B = A \times C$

**Make C the subject**

Multiply both sides by C: $A \times C = B \times \dfrac{\cancel{C}}{\cancel{C}}$

Divide both sides by A: $\cancel{A} \times \dfrac{C}{\cancel{A}} = \dfrac{B}{A}$

A cancels out on the left-hand side: $C = \dfrac{B}{A}$

---

**(1)** Tick ✓ the correct rearrangements of the equation below. Tick **two** boxes.

$$\text{concentration (g dm}^{-3}) = \frac{\text{mass of solute (g)}}{\text{volume of solution (dm}^3)}$$

A    $\text{mass of solute (g)} = \dfrac{\text{concentration (g dm}^{-3})}{\text{volume of solution (dm}^3)}$    ☐

B    $\text{mass of solute (g)} = \text{concentration (g dm}^{-3}) \times \text{volume of solution (dm}^3)$    ☐

C    $\text{volume of solution (dm}^3) = \dfrac{\text{mass of solute (g)}}{\text{concentration (g dm}^{-3})}$    ☐

D    $\text{volume of solution (dm}^3) = \dfrac{\text{concentration (g dm}^{-3})}{\text{mass of solute (g)}}$    ☐

---

To rearrange equations of the type $A = B \times C$

**Make B the subject**

Divide both sides by C: $\dfrac{A}{C} = B \times \dfrac{\cancel{C}}{\cancel{C}}$

C cancels out on the right-hand side: $B = \dfrac{A}{C}$

**Make C the subject**

Divide both sides by B: $\dfrac{A}{B} = \cancel{B} \times \dfrac{C}{\cancel{B}}$

B cancels out on the right-hand side: $C = \dfrac{A}{B}$

---

**(2)** The equation for mass is: mass of substance (g) = number of moles $\times$ $A_r$ or $M_r$
Using the method above, write 🖊 the equations for $A_r$ and for $M_r$.

You can also substitute the values into an equation and then solve it.

**(3)** Calculate 🖊 the mass of 0.6 mol of sodium using the equation:

$$\text{number of moles} = \frac{\text{mass of substance (g)}}{A_r} \qquad (A_r = 23)$$

mass = ..........................

**1    How do I set out calculations in a logical step-by-step way?**

Set your calculations out clearly, step by step, to help you check your method.

1  Here is a step-by-step checklist that will help you when doing a calculation. The steps are in the wrong order. Number 🖊 the steps in the correct order.

☐ Calculate your answer.

☐ Substitute the correct values into the equation.

☐ Highlight important information given in the question, including any values.

☐ Calculate any values you need to put into the equation. Show your working out and convert any units if necessary (e.g. kg to g).

☐ Write down your answer to an appropriate number of significant figures and include units.

☐ Write down any equations you need to use and rearrange them if necessary.

Now try using the steps to answer the following questions.

2  Calculate the mass of 0.030 mol of methane molecules, $CH_4$.
(relative atomic masses: C = 12, H = 1)

1  Highlight 🖊 the value for the number of moles you have been given in the question.

2  Write the equation and rearrange 🖊 it: number of moles = $\dfrac{\text{mass of substance (g)}}{M_r}$

Rearranged equation is: mass of substance (g) = .................................... × ....................

3  You do not need to convert any units. Calculate 🖊 the $M_r$ value for $CH_4$.

.................... + (.................... × ....................) = ....................

4  Substitute 🖊 the values into the equation: mass of substance = .................... × ....................

5  Calculate 🖊 the mass: mass = .................... g

6  Check that your answer has the correct number of significant figures (in this case, 2 sf) and that the unit is given.

3  Calculate the number of moles in 0.31 kg of sodium oxide, $Na_2O$.
(relative atomic masses: Na = 23, O = 16)

1  Highlight 🖊 the value for mass you have been given in the question.

2  Write 🖊 the equation.

3  a  Calculate 🖊 the $M_r$ value for $Na_2O$.

(.................... × ....................) + .................... = ....................

To convert kg to g multiply by 1000.

b  Convert 🖊 kg to g. 0.31 kg = .................... g

4  Substitute 🖊 the values into the equation: number of moles = $\dfrac{\text{....................}}{\text{....................}}$ g

5  Calculate 🖊 the number of moles: number of moles = ....................

6  Check that your answer has the correct number of significant figures (in this case, 2 sf).

## ② How do I give answers to an appropriate number of significant figures?

Using significant figures (sf) is a way of rounding to a given, or chosen, number of figures.

Sometimes you will be told how many significant figures to give your answer to. At other times you need to decide. You need to be able to round to an appropriate number of significant figures. This may be 1, 2 or 3 significant figures.

The first significant figure is the first non-zero digit (1–9) on the left of any number. Zero can be a significant figure if it appears to the right of the first significant figure.

① **a** Highlight 🖉 the **first** significant figure in these numbers: 0.0801, 24.9

**b** Highlight 🖉 the **second** significant figure in these numbers: 0.0801, 24.9

**c** Complete 🖉 this statement.

> 37.4 has 3 significant figures: ......................., ........................ and ...........................

**d** Complete 🖉 these sentences.

> When you round a number, if the next digit after the one you want is **5 or more**, round **up**. If the next digit is less than 5, do not round up.

> If you write 37.4 to 1 significant figure, then the first sf is .............. The next digit is 7,
>
> so you round 3 up to .............. You need to write a zero to keep the place value.
>
> So, 37.4 to 1 sf is ...............
>
> If you write 37.4 to 2 sf, then the second sf is .............. The next digit
>
> is 4, so .............. round up. 37.4 to 2 sf is ...............

You may be told how many significant figures to give. If not, look at the number of significant figures used in any values you are given. Give your answer to the smallest number of significant figures in these values.

② Write 🖉 the number of significant figures used in each value.

**a** relative atomic mass of copper, 63.5 ..................................

**b** mass of sodium chloride, 21 g ..................................

**c** a reaction time, 48.01 s ..................................

**d** moles of hydrochloric acid, 0.0033 mol ..................................

**e** moles of copper oxide, 5 mol ..................................

**f** Avogadro's constant, $6.02 \times 10^{23}$ mol$^{-1}$ ..................................

③ Complete 🖉 this table. The first row has been done for you.

| Number | To 1 sf | To 2 sf | To 3 sf |
|---|---|---|---|
| 0.02564 | 0.03 | 0.026 | 0.0256 |
| 0.00083921 | | | |
| 1.035 | | | |
| 609.72 | | | |

## 3 How do I calculate the mass of a reactant or product?

If you know the mass of one substance in a reaction, you can calculate the number of moles.

If you know the number of moles of one substance in a reaction and the mole ratio, you can work out the number of moles of the other substance. You can then calculate the mass of the other substance.

The mole ratio is the ratio of the number of moles of different substances shown in a balanced equation.

① The displacement reaction between copper sulfate and excess magnesium produces magnesium sulfate.

$$Mg(s) + CuSO_4(aq) \rightarrow MgSO_4(aq) + Cu(s)$$

Calculate the mass of magnesium sulfate produced from 319 g of copper sulfate.

Give your answer to two significant figures.

(relative atomic masses: Mg = 24, Cu = 63.5, S = 32, O = 16)

To solve this problem, you need to work through the following steps.
1. Calculate the number of moles of $CuSO_4$.
2. Use the balanced equation to find the mole ratio.
3. Work out the number of moles of $MgSO_4$.
4. Calculate the mass of $MgSO_4$.

a Look at the information you are given in the question.

Highlight ✐ the substances in the equation that are needed to answer the question.

b Calculate ✐ the relative formula mass of $CuSO_4$.

...................................................................................................................................

c Calculate ✐ the number of moles of $CuSO_4$ that reacted.

number of moles of $CuSO_4$ = ⬚/⬚ = ...................

To calculate the number of moles, use the equation:
number of moles
$= \dfrac{\text{mass of substance (g)}}{M_r}$

d Calculate ✐ the relative formula mass of $MgSO_4$.

...................................................................................................................................

e Find the mole ratio. ✐

From the balanced equation, 1 mol of $CuSO_4$ produces ............. mol of $MgSO_4$.

This gives a mole ratio of 1 : .............

f How many moles of $MgSO_4$ are produced in this reaction? ✐ .............

The number of moles of $MgSO_4$ produced in this reaction is the same as the number of moles of $CuSO_4$ that reacted.

g Calculate ✐ the mass of $MgSO_4$ produced.

mass = ...................................................................................................

To calculate the mass, use the equation: mass of substance (g)
= number of moles × $M_r$

② Another way to set out your answer is in a table.
Complete ✐ the table below.

Check how many significant figures your answer is given to.

| Substance | $CuSO_4$ | $MgSO_4$ |
|---|---|---|
| Mass (g) | 319 | |
| $M_r$ | | |
| Mole ratio | 1 | |
| Number of moles | | |

Look at any balancing numbers in front of the substances in the chemical equation.

The mass is either given in the question or it is what the question is asking for.

**Remember** The relative atomic masses of all atoms are listed in the periodic table.

**Unit 2 Chemistry calculations**    13

# Sample response

Use this student response to improve the way you answer calculations. Consider whether all the instructions have been followed and the working out has been shown in a step-by-step way.

## Exam-style question

1  Calculate the mass of 1.68 mol of lead nitrate $Pb(NO_3)_2$. Give your answer to three significant figures.

(relative atomic masses: Pb = 207, N = 14, O = 16)     **(2 marks)**

> $mass = moles \times M_r$
> $= 556.08 g$

① As you can see from the table, the student did not follow all the steps in the calculation.

|  | Has the student? | Have you? ✓ |
|---|---|---|
| Highlighted the important detail in the question. | no | |
| Shown the equation being used. | yes | |
| Shown the calculation for $M_r$. | no | |
| Substituted the values into the equation. | no | |
| Given the answer to the correct number of significant figures. | no | |

Using the table as a guide, write ✏ a more-detailed answer to the question. Tick ✓ the steps in the table as you do them.

# Your turn!

It is now time to use what you have learned to answer the exam-style question from page 9. Remember to read the question thoroughly, looking for information that may help you. Make good use of your knowledge from other areas of chemistry.

## Exam-style question

1   Ammonium sulfate is a salt used as a fertiliser.

Ammonia solution reacts with dilute sulfuric acid to produce ammonium sulfate.

$$2NH_3(aq) + H_2SO_4(aq) \rightarrow (NH_4)_2SO_4(aq)$$

(a)   Calculate the relative formula mass of sulfuric acid, $H_2SO_4$.

(relative atomic masses: N = 14, H = 1, O = 16, S = 32)          **(1 mark)**

Set out your working clearly to show how you get your answer.

relative formula mass = ............................................

(b)   Calculate the mass of ammonium sulfate produced when 3.4 g of ammonia reacts with excess sulfuric acid.

Give your answer to two significant figures.          **(3 marks)**

mass = ................................................ g

| Checklist - have you: | ⊘ |
|---|---|
| identified the information given to you? | |
| decided what to calculate? | |
| decided which equation you could use? | |
| set out your working clearly to show how you get your answer, including all the steps? | |
| given your answer to the correct number of significant figures? | |

# Need more practice?

Exam questions may ask about different parts of a topic, or parts of more than one topic. Questions about chemistry calculations could occur as part of a question on most chemistry topics, part of a question about an experiment or investigation, or as stand-alone questions.

Have a go at this exam-style question.

**Exam-style question**

1   Calculate the maximum mass of calcium nitrate that can be formed from 115 g of calcium carbonate and an excess of nitric acid.

$$CaCO_3(s) + 2HNO_3(aq) \rightarrow Ca(NO_3)_2(aq) + H_2O(l) + CO_2(g)$$

Give your answer to three significant figures.

(relative atomic masses: Ca = 40, C = 12, O = 16, H = 1, N = 14)          **(2 marks)**

mass = ...................................... g

**Boost your grade**

Every time you do a calculation in chemistry, write down your working-out in a logical way. Use the checklist on page 15 to help you. Practise making up your own calculations to help your understanding.

How confident do you feel about each of these **skills**? Colour in the bars.

① How do I set out calculations in a logical step-by-step way?

② How do I give answers to an appropriate number of significant figures?

③ How do I calculate the mass of a reactant or product?

# ③ Energy changes in reactions

This unit will help you understand energy changes in reactions.

**Exam-style question**

1   Methane burns completely in oxygen to form carbon dioxide and water.

$$CH_4 + 2O_2 \rightarrow CO_2 + 2H_2O$$

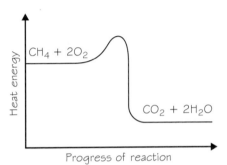

Figure 1

The reaction profile for this reaction is shown in Figure 1.

(a)   Explain how the reaction profile shows that this reaction is exothermic.        **(2 marks)**

(b)   Complete the reaction profile.

Draw labelled arrows to show:

- the overall heat energy change

- the activation energy.        **(2 marks)**

The bond energies and overall heat energy change are shown in Figure 2.

| Bond | C–O | C–H | H–H | O–H | C=O | Overall heat energy change |
|---|---|---|---|---|---|---|
| Bond energy (kJ mol⁻¹) | 358 | 413 | 436 | 464 | 805 | –818 |

Figure 2

(c)   Calculate the bond energy for the bond O=O using the equation for the reaction and the information in Figure 2.        **(3 marks)**

You will already have done some work on energy changes in reactions. Before starting the **skills boosts**, rate your confidence in each skill. Colour in 🖉 the bars.

❶ **How do I interpret reaction profiles?**

❷ **How do I draw reaction profiles?**

❸ **How do I calculate energy changes using bond energies?**

An **exothermic** reaction is one that transfers heat energy to the surroundings so the temperature of the surroundings increases.

An **endothermic** reaction is one that takes in heat energy from the surroundings so the temperature of the surroundings decreases.

**Remember** The 'surroundings' is everything other than the reacting substances themselves. This includes the water if it's a solution, the container and the air around the container.

You can work out whether the reaction is exothermic or endothermic by measuring the temperature change during a reaction.

Complete these activities to help prepare you for the topic.

**1** Tick ✓ to show which of the reactions below are endothermic and which are exothermic.

|  | Endothermic | Exothermic |
|---|---|---|
| Displacement reactions |  |  |
| Neutralisation reactions |  |  |
| Burning fuels |  |  |
| Precipitation reactions | ✓ | ✓ |

**2** Complete ✏ the table below.

A negative temperature change means that the temperature has decreased during the reaction.

| Reaction | Initial temperature (°C) | Final temperature (°C) | Temperature change (°C) | Exothermic or endothermic |
|---|---|---|---|---|
| 1 | 20 | 25 |  | exothermic |
| 2 | 20 | 17 |  |  |
| 3 | 21 |  | −36 |  |

**3** Complete ✏ these sentences by using words from the box below. You can use the words once, more than once or not at all.

| activation | particles | maximum | energy | minimum | collide | chemical | faster | slower |

Reactions can occur only when reacting particles ............................................ with each other with

sufficient energy. The ............................................ amount of energy that particles must have to react is

called the ............................................ energy. A reaction is ............................................ if the particles collide

more frequently and more particles have the ............................................ energy.

**4** What happens when the temperature of a reaction is increased? Circle Ⓐ the correct words.

a The particles will **gain / lose** energy

b A **lower / higher** proportion of the particles will have the activation energy.

c The particles will move **at the same speed / faster**.

d There will be **more / the same number of** collisions every second.

Use your answers to **4** to help you.

**5** What effect does increasing the temperature have on the rate of reaction? ✏

..............................................................................................................................................................

..............................................................................................................................................................

## 1 How do I interpret reaction profiles?

A reaction profile is used to model the energy change during a chemical reaction. In these diagrams, energy stored in the chemical bonds of the reactants and products is represented by horizontal lines. The higher the line, the greater the chemical energy stored in the bonds.

This diagram shows a simple reaction profile for chemical reactions **A** and **B**.

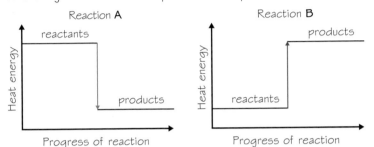

When using the term 'relative energy', it means you are comparing the amount of energy stored in different chemical bonds.

**1** Identify three statements that are true. Tick ✓ **three** boxes.

| | | |
|---|---|---|
| A | Reaction **A** is endothermic. | |
| B | In reaction **B**, the relative heat energy of the reactants is less than that of the products. | |
| C | In reaction **A**, heat energy is given out to the surroundings. | |
| D | In reaction **B**, the temperature of the surroundings will increase during the reaction. | |
| E | Reaction **A** is exothermic. | |
| F | In reaction **A**, the relative heat energy of the products is more than the relative heat energy of the reactants. | |

The graphs below show the reaction profiles for reactions **C** and **D**.

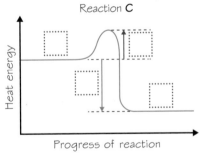

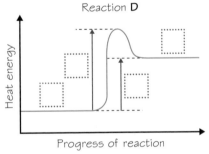

| | |
|---|---|
| A | reactants |
| B | products |
| C | temperature |
| D | activation energy |
| E | time |
| F | overall heat energy change |

**2** **a** Label 🖊 the reaction profiles for reactions **C** and **D** by writing letters from the box in the correct positions.

You may use each letter once, more than once or not at all.

The minimum energy needed for the particles to react and form products is shown by the 'hump' on the reaction profile.

**b** Complete 🖊 these sentences.

Reaction **C** is exothermic because heat energy is ............................................................ to the

surroundings and products have ............................................ heat energy relative to reactants.

**3** A catalyst is a substance that increases the rate of a reaction by reducing the activation energy. Complete these sentences by circling Ⓐ the correct words in each pair.

A catalyst reduces the activation energy for a reaction so **more / fewer** particles have the

activation energy. This makes the reaction **faster / slower**.

## 2 How do I draw reaction profiles?

A reaction profile can be drawn successfully by following three simple steps.

① Follow the steps below to draw a reaction profile on the axes provided.

**Step 1:** Work out if the reaction is exothermic or endothermic.

> The heat energy needed to break one mole of a particular covalent bond is the bond energy. It is measured in kilojoules per mole or kJ mol$^{-1}$.

**a** Which information can be used to determine whether a reaction is exothermic or endothermic? Tick ✓ **two** boxes.

A  The word equation ☐

B  Temperature change data ☐

C  Colour change observations ☐

D  Balanced symbol equation ☐

E  Bond energy data ☐

F  Bubbles being observed ☐

*y-axis: Heat energy*

*x-axis: Progress of reaction*

**Step 2:** Draw and label the reaction profile.

**b** Draw ✏ a line to show the relative heat energy of the reactants in an exothermic reaction.

**c** Draw ✏ a line to show the relative heat energy of the products in an exothermic reaction.

> **Remember** Leave a space between the two lines you draw so that the activation energy can be added in later.

**Step 3:** The activation energy is the minimum amount of energy needed by colliding particles for a reaction to occur. The activation energy is drawn as a 'hump' between the reactant and product lines.

**d** Draw ✏ a 'hump' to show the activation energy between the reactant and product lines.

② Here is some information about a reaction between citric acid and sodium hydrogencarbonate. Use the steps below to draw a profile for this reaction on paper.

> Citric acid was added to a solution of sodium hydrogencarbonate. The following observations were made:
>
>   Initial temperature of sodium hydrogencarbonate solution was 20°C.
>
>   Final temperature of the mixture after adding citric acid was 17°C.

**a** Complete the sentences by circling Ⓐ the correct word in each pair.

> The reaction is **exothermic / endothermic** because the temperature **decreased / increased** during the reaction. The relative heat energy of the reactants is **greater / less** than the relative heat energy of the products.

**b**  **i**  On paper, draw ✏ the axes for a reaction profile and label the x-axis and the y-axis.

**ii**  Draw ✏ a line to show the relative heat energy of the reactants in an endothermic reaction. Label this line 'reactants'.

**iii**  Draw ✏ a line to show the relative heat energy of the products in an endothermic reaction. Label this line 'products'.

**iv**  Draw ✏ a 'hump' between the reactant and product lines.

**v**  Add arrows and label ✏ the activation energy and the overall heat energy change.

## 3    How do I calculate energy changes using bond energies?

During a chemical reaction, bonds in the reactants break and new bonds are made to form the products. Bond energies can be used to calculate the overall heat energy changes for a reaction.

**(1)** Complete the sentences by circling Ⓐ the correct word in each pair.

> Breaking bonds requires heat energy. It is **endothermic / exothermic**.
>
> Making new bonds gives out heat energy. It is **endothermic / exothermic**.
>
> The **bond / chemical** energy is the energy needed to break a chemical bond or the energy
>
> given out when new bonds are made. The overall heat energy change in a reaction is
>
> **exothermic / endothermic** if more heat energy is released in forming bonds than is required
>
> in breaking bonds.

**(2)** A selection of bond energies are listed in the table.

Hydrogen gas reacts with chlorine gas to produce hydrogen chloride.

$H_2(g)$   +   $Cl_2(g)$   → ............. $HCl(g)$

H—H   +   Cl—Cl   → ........ H—Cl

| Bond | Bond energy (kJ mol$^{-1}$) |
|---|---|
| H—H | 436 |
| Cl—Cl | 242 |
| H—Cl | 431 |

**a**   Complete ✏ the equation above so that it balances.

**b**   Follow the steps below to calculate the energy change during the reaction.

> When balancing an equation, make sure that the number of atoms on each side of the equation is the same.

**Step 1:** Calculate ✏ the energy needed to break the bonds in the reactants.

| Bonds broken | Energy taken in |
|---|---|
| 1 × H—H | = ........................ kJ mol$^{-1}$ |
| 1 × Cl—Cl | = ........................ kJ mol$^{-1}$ |
| Total energy in | = ........................ kJ mol$^{-1}$ |

> When working out the number of bonds present, it is often helpful to write out all the covalent bonds in the formulae.

**Step 2:** Calculate ✏ the energy given out when the bonds are made in the products.

Bonds made        Energy given out

2 × H—Cl         = 2 × ........................ kJ mol$^{-1}$

Total energy out      = ........................ kJ mol$^{-1}$

**Step 3:** Calculate ✏ the overall energy change. Remember to include the units.

Energy change = energy in − energy out

         = ........................ − ........................ = ........................................

**c**   What does the negative sign in the answer show about the energy in and the energy out? ✏

...........................................................................................................................................................

...........................................................................................................................................................

**d**   Is the reaction endothermic or exothermic? ✏ ...........................................................................................

# Sample response

In the exam, questions about energy changes in reactions could ask you to draw or complete reaction profiles or carry out calculations using the bond energy data provided.

Use the student responses to these exam-style questions to improve your answers.

**Exam-style question**

1   Hydrogen reacts with oxygen to produce water.

The equation for the reaction is

$$2H_2 + O_2 \rightarrow 2H_2O$$
$$2H-H + O=O \rightarrow 2H-O-H$$

| Bond | Bond energy (kJ mol$^{-1}$) |
|------|------|
| H—H | 436 |
| O=O | 498 |
| O—H | 464 |

Figure 1

Figure 1 shows the bond energies for this reaction.

(a)   Use the information in Figure 1 to calculate the overall energy change.

> *Bonds broken = H—H and O=O. So energy in = 436 + 498 = 934 kJ mol$^{-1}$*
>
> *Bonds made = 2 x O—H. So energy out = 2 x 464 = 928 kJ mol$^{-1}$*
>
> *Energy change = energy in – energy out = 934 – 928 = 6 kJ mol$^{-1}$*

(b)   State whether the reaction is endothermic or exothermic.

> *Endothermic*

---

(**1**) The correct answer to (a) is –486 kJ mol$^{-1}$. The minus sign in the answer shows that this is an exothermic reaction. Identify 🖉 the two errors the student made in the calculation.

To make sure that you include all the bonds, draw out all the molecules and bonds in full and then count them up.

1   ....................................................................................................

....................................................................................................

2   ....................................................................................................

....................................................................................................

**Exam-style question**

2   Explain in terms of bond-making and bond-breaking why some reactions are endothermic.

> *If less energy is given out than taken in, then the reaction is endothermic.*

(**2**) Suggest 🖉 a way of improving the student answer.

.................................................................................................

.................................................................................................

.................................................................................................

.................................................................................................

.................................................................................................

A good answer will include which bonds are broken and which bonds are made. It will discuss the relative energies of the bonds involved in the reaction.

# Your turn!

It is now time to use what you have learned to answer the exam-style question from page 17. Remember to read the question thoroughly, looking for information that may help you. Make good use of your knowledge from other areas of chemistry.

### Exam-style question

1  Methane burns completely in oxygen to form carbon dioxide and water.

$$CH_4 + 2O_2 \rightarrow CO_2 + 2H_2O$$

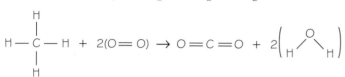

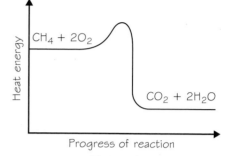

The reaction profile for this reaction is shown in Figure 1.

**Figure 1**

(a) Explain how the reaction profile shows that this reaction is exothermic. **(2 marks)**

......................................................................................................................................

......................................................................................................................................

......................................................................................................................................

(b) Complete the reaction profile by drawing in Figure 1 labelled arrows to show:

- the heat energy change

- the activation energy. **(2 marks)**

The bond energies and overall heat energy change are shown in Figure 2.

| Bond | C—O | C—H | H—H | O—H | C=O | Overall heat energy change |
|------|-----|-----|-----|-----|-----|-----|
| Bond energy (kJ mol⁻¹) | 358 | 413 | 436 | 464 | 805 | −818 |

**Figure 2**

(c) Calculate the bond energy for the bond O=O using the equation for the reaction and the information in Figure 2. **(3 marks)**

O=O represents one double bond and not two single bonds.

There are 2 molecules of oxygen in the chemical equation for the reaction so remember to divide the final answer by 2.

# Need more practice?

Questions about energy changes in reactions could occur as part of a question about equilibrium or rates of reaction, as part of a question about an experiment or investigation into temperature changes, or as a stand-alone question.

Have a go at these exam-style questions. Write ✏️ your answers on paper.

## Exam-style questions

1   Hydrogen is used to fuel rockets. Hydrogen burns in oxygen to produce water.

   (a)   Explain why a mixture of hydrogen and oxygen gas at room temperature and standard pressure does not react.                                **(2 marks)**

   (b)   In terms of bond energies, explain why hydrogen can be used as a fuel.   **(2 marks)**

2   Ammonia is made from nitrogen and hydrogen in the Haber process.

   The equation for the reaction is

   $$N_2(g) + 3H_2(g) \rightarrow 2NH_3(g)$$

   Look at the reaction profile shown in Figure 1.

   (a)   Describe how the heat energy changes during the reaction in Figure 1.   **(2 marks)**

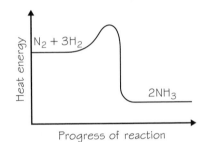

Figure 1

   The bond energies are shown in Figure 2.

   (b)   Calculate the overall heat energy change for the reaction.   **(3 marks)**

| Bond | Bond energy (kJ mol$^{-1}$) |
|------|------|
| H—H | 436 |
| N≡N | 945 |
| N—H | 391 |

Figure 2

## Boost your grade

More-challenging questions may involve more-complex chemical reactions, including the use of catalysts, making the reaction profiles more complex and bond energy calculations more demanding.

How confident do you feel about each of these **skills**? Colour in ✏️ the bars.

**1** How do I interpret reaction profiles?

**2** How do I draw reaction profiles?

**3** How do I calculate energy changes using bond energies?

# ④ Dynamic equilibrium

This unit will help you to understand dynamic equilibrium. It will also help you to apply knowledge and understanding of scientific ideas, scientific enquiry, techniques and procedures.

In the exam, you will be asked to answer questions such as the one below.

**Exam-style question**

1  Dinitrogen tetroxide, $N_2O_4$, is a colourless gas.

Nitrogen dioxide, $NO_2$, is a brown gas.

The equation for the reaction of a mixture of the two gases at equilibrium in a sealed container is

$$N_2O_4\,(g) \rightleftharpoons 2NO_2(g)$$

(a)  Explain what is meant by the term 'dynamic equilibrium'.          (2 marks)

(b)  Predict what you would observe in the mixture if the pressure in the container was increased.

Give a reason for your prediction.          (2 marks)

(c)  Explain why the mixture turns a deep brown colour when the reaction vessel is placed in a beaker of hot water.          (2 marks)

You will already have done some work on equilibrium. Before starting the **skills boosts**, rate your confidence for each skill. Colour in 🖉 the bars.

❶ How do I describe what dynamic equilibrium means?

❷ How do I predict changes in equilibrium position caused by temperature changes?

❸ How do I predict changes in equilibrium position caused by concentration or pressure changes?

For equilibrium to occur there must be a reversible reaction taking place in a closed system under certain conditions of temperature, concentration and pressure.

Changes in temperature, concentration or pressure will change the position of equilibrium. Generally, the equilibrium position moves in the direction that reduces the effect of the change in the closed system.

**(1)** A reversible reaction is a reaction in which the products can react to produce the original reactants.

For example, the decomposition of ammonium chloride is a reversible reaction:

ammonium chloride ⇌ hydrogen chloride + ammonia

**a** Write 🖉 the forward reaction.

..................................................................................

**b** Circle Ⓐ the reactants of the forward reaction.

**c** Draw 🖉 a box around the products of the forward reaction.

**d** Highlight 🖉 the reactants of the reverse reaction.

**e** Underline Ⓐ the products of the reverse reaction.

**f** Complete 🖉 the student's sentence below.

> Look at the direction of the half arrow. The forward reaction goes from left to right.

> The reactants of the forward reaction are .......................... as the products of the reverse reaction.

**(2)** Identify the closed systems. Tick ✓ **two** boxes.

> Nothing can get into or out of a closed system.

A   A conical flask with a tight-fitting bung. ☐

B   A boiling tube with a delivery tube. ☐

C   A beaker on a balance. ☐

D   A bottle with a screw top. ☐

**(3)** Draw 🖉 linking lines to complete **four** sentences. One has been done for you.

a   heat energy is taken in from the surroundings

A   During an exothermic reaction — b   the temperature increases

c   the temperature decreases

B   During an endothermic reaction

d   there is no change in heat energy

e   heat energy is given out to the surroundings

> 'Exo' means 'out' as in exit and 'endo' means 'in' as in entrance, so exothermic means heat is transferred out, endothermic means heat is transferred in.

**(4)** The diagram shows the particles in different mixtures at different concentrations.

A          B          C

Write 🖉 a letter in the box to identify the mixture with:

**a** the lowest concentration of ● ☐      **b** the highest concentration of ● ☐

**1** **How do I describe what dynamic equilibrium means?**

At dynamic equilibrium both the forward and the reverse reactions are constantly occurring at the same rate.

When ammonia is made from nitrogen and hydrogen gas the reaction reaches dynamic equilibrium:

$$N_2(g) + 3H_2(g) \rightleftharpoons 2NH_3(g)$$

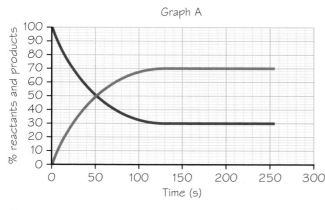

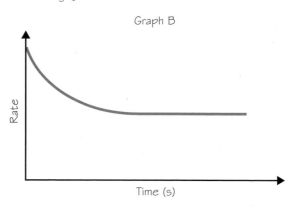

① The graphs show the reaction of nitrogen and hydrogen to produce ammonia.

Graph A shows how the percentage of reactants and products of the forward reaction change over time.

Graph B shows how the rate of the forward reaction changes over time.

> The rate of a reaction is the speed at which reactants are turned into products.

**a** One line on graph A shows how the amount of reactants changes over time. Label this line **R**.

> Think about what happens to the reactants during the reaction.

**b** One line on graph A shows how the amount of products changes over time. Label this line **P**.

**c** On each line on graph A, write **E** at the point when dynamic equilibrium is reached.

> Equilibrium means 'in balance'. Dynamic means that there is 'constant change'.

**d** Draw another line on graph B to show how the rate of the reverse reaction changes with time.

② Circle Ⓐ the correct words or phrases in **bold** to complete these sentences.

> At dynamic equilibrium the amount of substances in a closed system **increases / remains the same / decreases**. This is because the rate of the forward reaction is **more than / equal to / less than** the rate of the reverse reaction.

> You need to think about what is happening at the particle level in a reaction that looks as though it is staying the same.

## ② How do I predict changes in equilibrium position caused by temperature changes?

When a reaction is in dynamic equilibrium, the relative amounts of reactants and products in the reaction vessel stay the same. Changing the temperature of the system changes the position of equilibrium and so the relative amounts of reactants and products also change.

> If a dynamic equilibrium is disturbed by changing the conditions, the equilibrium position shifts to reduce the effect of the change.

When the temperature is increased, the equilibrium shifts in the direction of the **endothermic** reaction. It transfers energy from the surroundings, cooling them down.

When the temperature is decreased, the equilibrium shifts to the direction of the **exothermic** reaction. It transfers energy to the surroundings, heating them up.

① The diagram shows a reaction that is in dynamic equilibrium.

forward reaction

$$H_2(g) + I_2(g) \rightleftharpoons 2HI(g)$$

reverse reaction

a The forward reaction is exothermic.

The reverse reaction is endothermic.

Write ✏ the words exothermic and endothermic on the correct arrows in the diagram.

b Complete ✏ the table to predict what happens to the amount of hydrogen iodide in the reaction vessel in each situation.

| Reaction situation | Amount of hydrogen iodide |
|---|---|
| At dynamic equilibrium | It stays the same |
| The position of equilibrium moves to the left | |
| The position of equilibrium moves to the right | |

Look at the chemical equation. When the position of equilibrium moves, it favours the reaction in the direction it is moving OR the rate of the reaction in the direction it moves increases.

c Circle Ⓐ the correct words in **bold** to complete these sentences.

> Decreasing the temperature moves the position of equilibrium in the direction of the **endothermic / exothermic** reaction in order to increase the temperature again.
>
> **Increasing / Decreasing** the temperature moves the position of equilibrium in the direction of the endothermic reaction.

② Complete ✏ the table for the reaction below which is in dynamic equilibrium.

$$CO(g) + 2H_2(g) \rightleftharpoons CH_3OH(g)$$

| Temperature change | Effect on position of equilibrium | Reason |
|---|---|---|
| Increase | | The forward reaction is exothermic and the reaction changes to decrease the temperature. |
| | Moves to the right. | |

**3** **How do I predict changes in equilibrium position caused by concentration or pressure changes?**

The position of a dynamic equilibrium changes if the concentration of a reactant or product is changed. This alters the relative amounts of reactants and products at equilibrium. The position of equilibrium shifts to reduce the effects of any changes to the system.

If the concentration of a substance is increased, the equilibrium shifts in the direction that uses up the substance that has been added.

If the concentration of a substance is decreased, the equilibrium shifts in the direction that forms more of it.

1 The diagram shows the particles of some substances in dynamic equilibrium.

   a If more ● are added, how will the system react to restore the equilibrium?

   Tick ✓ **one** box.

   Produce more ● and equilibrium position moves left.

   Produce more ● and equilibrium position moves left.

   Produce more ● and equilibrium position moves right.

   Shift the position of equilibrium towards the left.

   **Remember** The system is closed so no other particles can enter or leave the system on their own.

   **Remember** The equilibrium position shifts to reduce the effects of any changes to the system.

   b If ● are removed, how will the system react to restore the equilibrium?

   Tick ✓ **one** box.

   Produce more ● + ● and position of equilibrium moves left.

   Produce more ● and position of equilibrium moves right.

   The position of equilibrium will stay the same.

When working with gases, the pressure can also change the position of equilibrium.

2 Complete these sentences about the reaction between nitrogen and hydrogen to form ammonia.

$$N_2(g) + 3H_2(g) \rightleftharpoons 2NH_3(g)$$

Increasing the pressure moves the ............................................................ to the side with the ............................................ number of molecules.

On the left-hand side of the equation there are ........................................... molecules of gas. On the right-hand side of the equation there are ........................................... molecules of gas. More molecules produce more pressure, so an increase in pressure will move the position of equilibrium to the ............................................. This would result in an increase in ............................................ molecules.

# Sample response

Here are some exam-style questions. Use the student responses to these questions to improve your understanding of dynamic equilibrium.

---

**Exam-style question**

1   An equilibrium forms between chlorine and two different iodine chlorides:

$$ICl(l) \quad + \quad Cl_2(g) \quad \rightleftharpoons \quad ICl_3(s)$$

dark brown            green            yellow

(a)   Describe **two** conditions needed for dynamic equilibrium to occur.          **(2 marks)**

---

Here is one student's response.

A   | Rate of the reactions is the same. |

Describe means recall some facts. In this question you must recall two facts.

Here is another student's answer.

B   | In a closed system the rate of the forward reaction is equal to the rate of the reverse reaction. |

① Give 🖊 **two** reasons why student B gains more marks than student A.

a   .......................................................................................................................................

   .......................................................................................................................................

   .......................................................................................................................................

b   .......................................................................................................................................

   .......................................................................................................................................

   .......................................................................................................................................

---

**Exam-style question**

(b)   When the equilibrium mixture is heated, the colour becomes a darker brown.

Explain whether the reverse reaction is endothermic or exothermic.          **(2 marks)**

---

Here is one student's answer.

C   | Endothermic because the reverse reaction is favoured by higher temperatures. |

Here is another student's response.

D   | Endothermic because the reverse reaction lowers the temperature. |

You need to apply the rule that the equilibrium position shifts to reduce the effects of changes to the system.

② Why do you think student C was awarded 2 marks but student D was only awarded 1 mark? 🖊

.......................................................................................................................................

.......................................................................................................................................

# Your turn!

It is now time to use what you have learned to answer the exam-style question from page 25. Remember to read the question thoroughly, looking for information that may help you. Make good use of your knowledge from other areas of chemistry.

**Exam-style question**

1    Dinitrogen tetroxide, $N_2O_4$, is a colourless gas.

Nitrogen dioxide, $NO_2$, is a brown gas.

The equation for the reaction of a mixture of the two gases at equilibrium in a sealed container is:

$$N_2O_4(g) \rightleftharpoons 2NO_2(g)$$

(a)    Explain what is meant by the term 'dynamic equilibrium'.          **(2 marks)**

..................................................................................

..................................................................................

..................................................................................

..................................................................................

..................................................................................

| An answer to an explain question needs a reason. |

| You need to consider both the forward and reverse reactions. |

(b)    Predict what you would observe in the mixture if the pressure in the container was increased. Give a reason for your prediction.          **(2 marks)**

| Look at the total number of molecules of gas on each side of the equation. |

..................................................................................

..................................................................................

| You need to predict **and** give a reason. |

..................................................................................

..................................................................................

..................................................................................

..................................................................................

(c)    Explain why the mixture turns a deep brown colour when the reaction vessel is placed in a beaker of hot water.          **(2 marks)**

..................................................................................

..................................................................................

| Use the colour change to work out which way the position of equilibrium has moved. |

..................................................................................

..................................................................................

..................................................................................

# Need more practice?

Questions about dynamic equilibrium could occur as part of a question about rates of reaction, part of a question about industrial processes such as the manufacture of ammonia, or as stand-alone questions.

Have a go at these exam-style questions.

## Exam-style questions

1  Fizzy drinks are made by forcing carbon dioxide gas into the drink under high pressure.

   This causes the $CO_2(g)$ to dissolve in the drink to form $CO_2(aq)$.

   A dynamic equilibrium is established in an unopened bottle:     $CO_2(g) \rightleftharpoons CO_2(aq)$

   (a)  Compare the rate of the forward and reverse reactions when the drinks bottle is closed.

        Suggest a reason for your answer.                                    **(2 marks)**

   ....................................................................................................................

   ....................................................................................................................

   (b)  Predict what will happen to the position of equilibrium when the bottle is opened.

        Give a reason for your answer.                                       **(2 marks)**

   ....................................................................................................................

   ....................................................................................................................

2  Sulfuric acid is manufactured in different stages.

   In one stage, sulfur dioxide, $SO_2$, is converted to sulfur trioxide, $SO_3$, in an exothermic reaction.

   The equation for the reaction is:          $2SO_2(g) + O_2(g) \rightleftharpoons 2SO_3(g)$

   (a)  Explain why a pressure of 200 atmospheres would most favour the forward reaction.  **(2 marks)**

   ....................................................................................................................

   ....................................................................................................................

   (b)  Explain the effect of increasing temperature on this reaction.                **(2 marks)**

   ....................................................................................................................

   ....................................................................................................................

## Boost your grade

You may be asked to interpret graphs and other data in a range of different contexts.

How confident do you feel about each of these **skills**? Colour in  the bars.

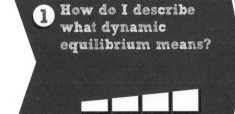

1  **How do I describe what dynamic equilibrium means?**

2  **How do I predict changes in equilibrium position caused by temperature changes?**

3  **How do I predict changes in equilibrium position caused by concentration or pressure changes?**

# (5) Organic chemistry

This unit will help you to draw and recognise the structures of alkenes, alcohols and carboxylic acids. It will also help you understand how some organic substances react in addition reactions and how some types of polymers are formed.

In the exam, you will be asked to name or draw the structure for some alkenes, alcohols and carboxylic acids. You will need to draw structures for the addition reactions of alkenes and write chemical equations for some of the reactions that organic compounds undergo. You will need to be able to answer questions such as the ones below.

## Exam-style questions

1   Ethene is a hydrocarbon.
    (a)   Draw the structure of a molecule of ethene ($C_2H_4$), showing all the covalent bonds.  **(1 mark)**
    (b)   Describe how ethene molecules can combine together in a polymerisation reaction.  **(2 marks)**

2   The structure of an organic compound **X** is shown as:

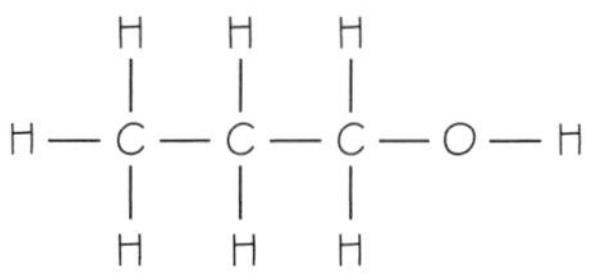

    (a)   Name compound **X**.  **(1 mark)**
    (b)   Circle the functional group in the structure
          of compound **X**.  **(1 mark)**

3   Alkenes undergo addition reactions with bromine.
    (a)   Propene is an alkene. The structure of propene is shown as:
          Circle the functional group in propene.  **(1 mark)**

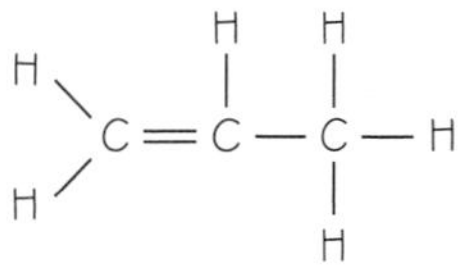

    (b)   Draw the structures of the products of the addition reactions of
          but-1-ene and but-2-ene with bromine, showing all the covalent bonds.

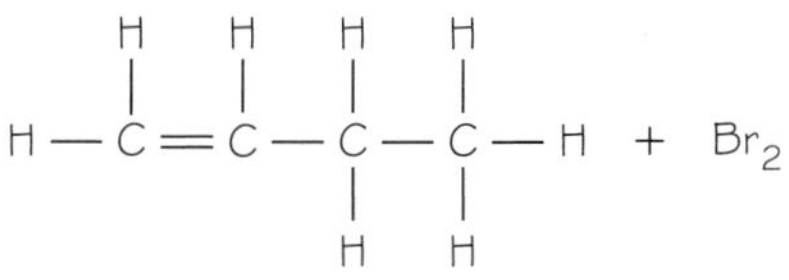

          But-1-ene 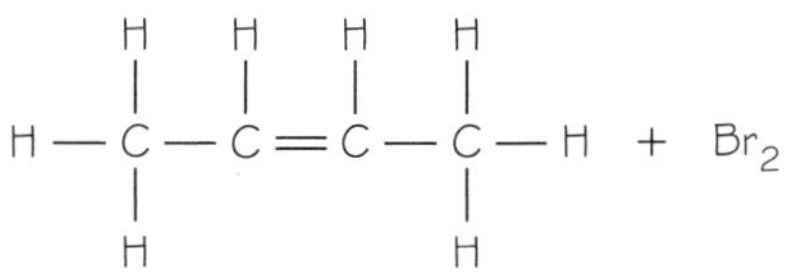                          But-2-ene                    **(2 marks)**

    (c)   Explain how bromine water is used to distinguish between butene and butane.  **(2 marks)**

You will already have done some work on organic chemistry. Before starting the
**skills boosts**, rate your confidence in each area below. Colour in ✏ the bars.

| **1** How do I draw the structures of alkenes, alcohols and carboxylic acids, showing all covalent bonds? | **2** How do I draw the structures of the products of addition reactions, showing all covalent bonds? | **3** How do I explain polymerisation? |
|---|---|---|

A **homologous series** is a family of organic molecules that have the same general formula, and similar chemical properties. Alkenes, alcohols and carboxylic acids are homologous series. Each homologous series has a different functional group.

**Remember** Organic molecules contain carbon atoms arranged in rings or chains.

A **functional group** is the reactive atom, group of atoms or chemical bond in a molecule. For example, the alkenes have a C=C functional group, the alcohols have –OH and the carboxylic acids have –COOH.

Organic compounds are named using a **suffix** that shows the homologous series they belong to. For example, butanol and ethanol have ol as a suffix and belong to the alcohols.

**1** **a** **i** Draw 🖊 lines to match each suffix to its homologous series.

**ii** Draw 🖊 lines to match each homologous series with its functional group.

| Suffix | Homologous series | Functional group |
|--------|-------------------|------------------|
| ene | alkenes | –OH |
| ol | carboxylic acids | C=C |
| oic acid | alcohols | –COOH |

The –COOH group can be written as

$$— C{=}O$$
$$|$$
$$O — H$$

Don't confuse the –COOH functional group with the –OH functional group.

**b** Complete 🖉 these sentences.

Propene has ene as a suffix and belongs to the ........................................... . Methanoic acid

has ........................................ as a suffix and belongs to the .............................................. .

**c** Complete 🖉 the table by circling the suffix in each of the compounds and writing the correct homologous series and functional group.

| Compound | Homologous series | Functional group |
|----------|-------------------|------------------|
| propene | | |
| ethanoic acid | | |
| propanol | | |
| butene | | |

**2** Organic compounds also have a prefix in their name to show the number of carbon atoms.

butanol

prefix contains 4 carbon atoms

suffix belongs to the alcohols

| number of carbon atoms present | 1 | 2 | 3 | 4 |
|--------------------------------|------|-----|------|-----|
| prefix | meth | eth | prop | but |

Complete 🖉 the sentences below.

Propanol has the prefix prop and contains ........................................

carbon atoms, it has the suffix ol and belongs to the alcohols. Ethanoic

acid contains ........................................ carbon atoms, it has the suffix

........................................ and belongs to the .............................................. .

Butene contains ........................................ carbon atoms, it has the suffix

........................................ and belongs to the .............................................. .

To help you remember the order of these prefixes, remember **m**onkeys **e**at **p**eanut **b**utter **p**ies.

Look at the prefix and suffix in each name and use the table above to find the number of carbon atoms.

> **1** **How do I draw the structures of alkenes, alcohols and carboxylic acids, showing all covalent bonds?**

Organic chemistry is the chemistry of carbon compounds, with the exception of carbon dioxide, carbon monoxide and carbonates. The structure of a molecule showing all covalent bonds can be written for all organic compounds. Lines are used to represent the covalent bonds between individual atoms.

**①** Carbon is in group 4 of the periodic table and has four electrons in its outer shell so its atoms form **four** covalent bonds in its compounds. Answer the questions below to name the organic molecules **A**, **B** and **C**.

> Each line represents a covalent bond, so two lines represent two covalent bonds (double bond). You can check the number of bonds for each atom by counting them.

```
    H   H   H   H              H   H                    H   H   H
    |   |   |   |              |   |                    |   |   |
H — C — C — C = C          H — C — C — O — H        H — C — C — C — C = O
    |   |                      |   |                    |   |   |
    H   H                      H   H                    H   H   H   O — H

         A                          B                          C
```

**ⓐ** Circle Ⓐ the functional group in **A**, **B** and **C**.

**ⓑ** Write 🖉 the functional groups for **A**, **B** and **C** in the table. One has been done for you.

> **Remember** —OH, —COOH and C=C are the alcohol, carboxylic acid and alkene functional groups.

**ⓒ** Use the functional groups to write 🖉 the suffix for each molecule. One has been done for you.

**ⓓ** Count the number of carbon atoms present in **A**, **B** and **C** and write 🖉 this in the table.

**ⓔ** Use the number of carbon atoms to write 🖉 the prefix for each molecule.

> When drawing acids, the carbon of the —COOH functional group is included in the total number of carbon atoms present.

**ⓕ** Complete 🖉 the table by using the prefix and suffix to name molecules **A**, **B** and **C**.

| | Number of carbon atoms present | Prefix | Functional group present | Suffix | Name |
|---|---|---|---|---|---|
| A | | | C=C | ene | |
| B | | | | | |
| C | | | | | |

**②** Draw the formula for butanol, showing all the covalent bonds, by answering the questions below.

**ⓐ** What is the prefix in butanol? 🖉 .............................................

**ⓑ** How many carbon atoms are present in butanol? 🖉 ....................     Use the prefix.

**ⓒ** What is the suffix in butanol? 🖉 .............................................

**ⓓ** What is the functional group? 🖉 .............................................

**ⓔ** Complete 🖉 the structure in the box by adding the correct number of carbon atoms and then the functional group.

**ⓕ** Draw 🖉 single bonds to make sure every carbon has 4 bonds.

**ⓖ** Add hydrogen atoms to each bond.

> C–C

**2** **How do I draw the structures of the products of addition reactions, showing all covalent bonds?**

An **addition reaction** is one in which two molecules react to form one single product. Alkenes are unsaturated as they contain at least one carbon–carbon double bond, C=C. Alkenes can undergo addition reactions because the C=C bond breaks open and atoms add on to the two carbon atoms. We say the molecule 'adds across the double bond'. The product is an alkane, contains a C–C single bond and is saturated.

**Saturated** (in the context of organic chemistry) means that all the carbon–carbon bonds are single.

**1** Complete ✏ the table by writing the phrases or words below in the correct column.

saturated     unsaturated     contains single C–C bonds only

contains a C=C bond     undergoes addition reactions     does not undergo addition reactions

| Propane | Propene |
|---|---|
|  |  |
|  |  |
|  |  |

**2** The equation shows an addition reaction. The circles represent atoms.

alkene      molecule reacting      product

**a** Colour in ✏ the atoms of the molecule reacting with the alkene.

**b** In the reaction, the C=C bond breaks open and the two atoms you have coloured add on, one to each carbon. In the product, colour in ✏ two atoms, one on each carbon, to show how the molecule has added on across the double bond.

**3** Propene reacts in an addition reaction with bromine. Answer the questions to write an equation using the formula showing all the covalent bonds for the reaction.

**a** Complete ✏ the structure of propene in the box on the left.

C=C—C     + Br—Br ⟶

**b** For the product, draw ✏ the original organic compound in the box on the right (propene) but with a C–C bond instead of C=C. All bonds should be at 90°.

**c** Now draw ✏ the fourth bond on each carbon and attach an atom from the molecule reacting ($Br_2$).

Addition reactions always take place across the double bond.

# 3 How do I explain polymerisation?

A **polymer** is a large molecule made from lots of small molecules, called **monomers**, joined together. The process in which monomers join together is called **polymerisation**.

A polymer has a high average molecular mass, anything from tens of thousands to millions. The polymer chains are not given specific relative molecular masses because they vary in length. When monomers such as ethene join together, one of the bonds in the double bond opens out and joins to the next ethene molecule. This process is called **addition** polymerisation.

① The equation below shows an addition polymerisation reaction. The circles represent atoms.

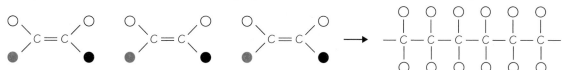

**a** Circle Ⓐ a monomer.

**b** In the reaction, the C=C bond breaks open and joins to the next molecule. In the polymer product, colour in 🖉 red and black atoms to show how the molecules have joined together.

> Count the number of carbon atoms in a monomer molecule.

**c** Highlight 🖉 a repeating unit in the product.

This reaction can be written as an equation:

**d** Why is there an 'n' next to the square brackets? 🖉

.................................................................................................

.................................................................................................

> n is a very large number

② When ethene molecules join together, poly(ethene) is formed.

**a** Complete 🖉 the sentences.

> Look back at page 35.

During polymerisation of ethene, a C=C bond ........................................ and another ........................................ ........................................ joins on. This happens again and again until a long ........................................ is formed.

**b** Complete 🖉 the equation for the formation of poly(ethene).

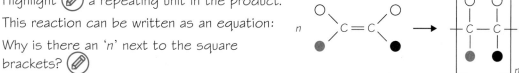

> The word 'poly' means many.

③ Complete 🖉 the table to show that there are many different types of polymers made from different monomers.

| Name of polymer | Monomer | Repeating unit |
|---|---|---|
|  | Propene  H₂C=CH—CH₃ (drawn structure) |  |
| Poly(chloroethene) | Chloroethene  H₂C=CHCl (drawn structure) |  |

> To work out the monomer, look at the repeating unit to work out where the double bond should go.

> To work out the repeating unit, look at the monomer and break open the double bond. Don't forget the square brackets.

# Sample response

When drawing the structure for alkenes, alcohols and carboxylic acids you should:
- use the prefix to determine the number of carbon atoms present: meth, eth, prop, but
- use the suffix to determine the functional group present: –OH, C=C or –COOH
- represent covalent bonds by lines, and ensure that each carbon has four bonds.

**Exam-style question**

1  Which structure, **A, B, C** or **D**, shows butanoic acid?

A

```
    H   H   H   H
    |   |   |   |
H — C — C — C — C — O — H
    |   |   |   |
    H   H   H   H
```

B

```
    H   H   H
    |   |   |
H — C — C — C — O — H
    |   |   |
    H   H   H
```

C

```
    H   H
    |   |
H — C — C — C = O
    |   |   |
    H   H   O — H
```

D

```
    H   H   H
    |   |   |
H — C — C — C — C = O
    |   |   |   |
    H   H   H   O — H
```

Here is one student's answer to the exam-style question.  ☐ D

① Why are **A** and **B** incorrect? Use the following steps to help you answer this.

**a**  Circle Ⓐ the functional group in **A** and **B** .

**b**  What is the suffix that should be used when naming **A** and **B**? 🖉 ................................................................

For **C** to be incorrect, it must have either the wrong functional group or the wrong number of carbons.

**c**  Circle Ⓐ the functional group in **C**.

**d**  What is the suffix that should be used when naming **C**? 🖉 ................................................................

**e**  Is it the correct suffix for butanoic acid? Ⓐ **Yes / No**

**f**  Count the carbon atoms in **C**. 🖉 ................................................................

**g**  What is the prefix that should be used for **C**? 🖉 ................................................................

**h**  Is it the correct prefix for butanoic acid? Ⓐ **Yes / No**

**i**  Is the student's answer correct? Ⓐ **Yes / No**

> **Remember** The carbon of the –COOH functional group is included in the total number of carbon atoms present.

**Exam-style question**

2  Draw the structure of the following organic compounds, showing all the covalent bonds.

(a) propene   (b) propanoic acid   (c) butanol

Here is one student's answer.

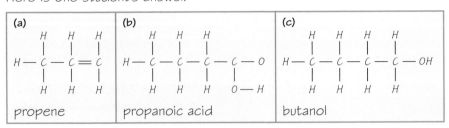

| (a) | (b) | (c) |
|---|---|---|
| ```    H   H   H    |   |   | H — C — C = C    |   |   |    H   H   H``` | ```    H   H   H    |   |   | H — C — C — C — C — O    |   |   |    H   H   H   O — H``` | ```    H   H   H   H    |   |   |   | H — C — C — C — C — OH    |   |   |   |    H   H   H   H``` |
| propene | propanoic acid | butanol |

> **Remember** Carbon only forms 4 bonds.

> Look at the prefix and count the number of carbon atoms. Check the functional group.

② Look at the student's answer to this exam-style question and, on paper, list 🖉 four errors.

# Your turn!

It is now time to use what you have learned to answer the exam-style questions from page 33. Remember to read the question thoroughly, looking for information that may help you. Make good use of your knowledge from other areas of chemistry.

## Exam-style questions

**1** Ethene is a hydrocarbon.

(a) Draw the structure of a molecule of ethene ($C_2H_4$), showing all the covalent bonds. **(1 mark)**

(b) Describe how ethene molecules can combine together in a polymerisation reaction. **(2 marks)**

....................................................................................................

....................................................................................................

....................................................................................................

> The double bond in ethene is really important here.

**2** The structure of an organic compound **X** is shown as:

(a) Name compound **X**. **(1 mark)**

....................................................................................................

$$H-\underset{\underset{H}{|}}{\overset{\overset{H}{|}}{C}}-\underset{\underset{H}{|}}{\overset{\overset{H}{|}}{C}}-\underset{\underset{H}{|}}{\overset{\overset{H}{|}}{C}}-O-H$$

**X**

(b) Circle the functional group in the structure of compound **X**. **(1 mark)**

**3** Alkenes undergo addition reactions with bromine.

(a) Propene is an alkene. The structure of propene is shown as: Circle the functional group in propene. **(1 mark)**

$$\underset{H}{\overset{H}{>}}C=C-\underset{\underset{H}{|}}{\overset{\overset{H}{|}}{C}}-H$$

> The C=C breaks and one atom of the molecule reacting with butene adds on to each carbon.

(b) Draw the structure of the products of the addition reactions of but-1-ene and but-2-ene with bromine, showing all the covalent bonds.

$$H-C=C-\underset{\underset{H}{|}}{\overset{\overset{H}{|}}{C}}-\underset{\underset{H}{|}}{\overset{\overset{H}{|}}{C}}-H \ + \ Br_2 \longrightarrow$$

But-1-ene

> Remember that alkanes only contain carbon–carbon single bonds.

$$H-\underset{\underset{H}{|}}{\overset{\overset{H}{|}}{C}}-C=C-\underset{\underset{H}{|}}{\overset{\overset{H}{|}}{C}}-H \ + \ Br_2 \longrightarrow$$

But-2-ene

**(2 marks)**

(c) Explain how bromine water is used to distinguish between butene and butane. **(2 marks)**

....................................................................................................

....................................................................................................

# Need more practice?

Questions about organic chemistry could occur as part of a question on crude oil, ethanol or reactions of acids, part of a question about an experiment, or as stand-alone questions.

Have a go at these exam-style questions.

## Exam-style questions

1 The structure of pentene is shown as:
$$H-C=C-C-C-C-H$$
with H atoms shown on the structure

(a) Pentene undergoes an addition reaction with bromine. Draw the structure of a molecule of the product formed, showing all the covalent bonds.  **(1 mark)**

(b) Name the product of the addition reaction of pentene with bromine.  **(1 mark)**

................................................................

When 2 bromine atoms are added into the structure, the name starts with dibromo.

2 Complete the equation for the polymerisation of butene.  **(1 mark)**

(a)
$$n \quad H-C-C-C=C \longrightarrow$$
with H atoms shown on the structure

(b) Name the polymer formed.  **(1 mark)**

................................................................

3 Complete the structure of a molecule of ethanoic acid, showing all the covalent bonds.  **(1 mark)**

$$H-C-C$$

## Boost your grade

To improve your grade, you should be able to describe how the first four carboxylic acids:

• react with carbonates, dissolve in water, and react with alcohols to form esters
• react with sodium, dissolve in water and react with an oxidising agent.

You do not need to write chemical equations for these reactions.

How confident do you feel about each of these **skills**? Colour in  the bars.

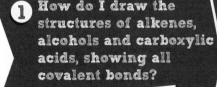

① How do I draw the structures of alkenes, alcohols and carboxylic acids, showing all covalent bonds?

② How do I draw the structures of the products of addition reactions, showing all covalent bonds?

③ How do I explain polymerisation?

# ⑥ Chemical analysis

This unit will help you to understand how to identify the ions present in a compound.

**Exam-style question**

1  A student investigated three solutions. The solutions were aluminium chloride, calcium carbonate and iron(II) sulfate.

(a)  The student carried out two tests.

The results are shown in Figure 1.

Complete Figure 1.                                                                                    (3 marks)

| Test | Aluminium chloride solution | Calcium carbonate solution | Iron(II) sulfate solution |
|---|---|---|---|
| adding dilute nitric acid followed by silver nitrate | | no change | no change |
| adding dilute hydrochloric acid followed by barium chloride | | | white precipitate |

Figure 1

(b)  Explain why the student added dilute acid in each of the tests.                 (1 mark)

(c)  Write an ionic equation for the reaction between barium ions and sulfate ions. Include state symbols.                                                                              (3 marks)

(d)  In another experiment to identify the metal ion present in each solution, the student carried out flame tests and added sodium hydroxide solution to the metal ion solutions.

The results of the tests are shown in Figure 2. Complete Figure 2.             (5 marks)

| | Aluminium chloride | Calcium carbonate | Iron(II) sulfate |
|---|---|---|---|
| flame test | no colour | | no colour |
| adding sodium hydroxide solution | | white precipitate | |
| adding excess sodium hydroxide solution | | | no change |

Figure 2

You will already have done some work on chemical analysis. Before starting the **skills boosts**, rate your confidence in each area. Colour in 🖉 the bars.

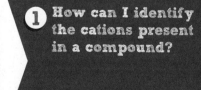

① **How can I identify the cations present in a compound?**

② **How can I identify the anions present in a compound?**

③ **How can I use chemical tests to identify the ions in unknown single ionic compounds?**

An ion is a particle that has a charge. A cation is a positive ion. An anion is a negative ion.

**Remember** The names of negative ions of **elements** end in '-ide'.

1 Complete 🖊 the table. The first two rows have been done for you.

**Remember** If an ion's name ends in '-ate' it contains oxygen: sulfate $SO_4^{2-}$ contains oxygen; sulfide $S^{2-}$ does not.

| Ion name | Ion formula | Cation | Anion |
|---|---|---|---|
| calcium | $Ca^{2+}$ | ✓ | |
| sulfate | $SO_4^{2-}$ | | ✓ |
| hydroxide | | | |
| | $CO_3^{2-}$ | | |
| sodium | | | |
| | $Cl^-$ | | |

2 Ionic compounds contain a cation and an anion.

When writing formulae, the charges on the positive ions must equal the charges on the negative ions.

a Complete 🖊 the table below.

| Compound name | Compound formula | Name and formula of the cation present | Name and formula of the anion present |
|---|---|---|---|
| calcium sulfate | $CaSO_4$ | calcium $Ca^{2+}$ | sulfate $SO_4^{2-}$ |
| potassium chloride | | | |
| | $CuCO_3$ | | |
| | | lithium $Li^+$ | iodide $I^-$ |

b There are three errors in the sentence below. Highlight 🖊 the errors and correct them.

> Copper chloride contains positive chloride ions and a negative copper ion. Its formula is CuCl.

3 a A flame test can be carried out to test for the presence of some cations. Draw 🖊 lines to match the cation with the correct flame colour.

Cation

| $Li^+$ |
| $Cu^{2+}$ |
| $K^+$ |
| $Ca^{2+}$ |
| $Na^+$ |

Flame colour

| yellow |
| lilac |
| orange-red |
| green |
| crimson |

**Remember** A flame colour is produced by the metal ion in the compound. Don't confuse flame colours with the colour of the flame when a metal burns in air. For some metals, the colour is the same, but in others it is not. You need to learn these flame test colours.

b The steps to carry out a flame test are listed below, but they are not in the correct order.

Write 🖊 the letters of the steps in the correct order: ☐ ☐ ☐ ☐

A Dip the nichrome wire loop into the sample to be tested.

B Record the flame colour.

C Place the nichrome wire loop and sample into a blue Bunsen flame.

D Dip a nichrome wire loop into hydrochloric acid.

# 1 How can I identify the cations present in a compound?

Flame tests can be used to identify the metal cation in some compounds. A flame photometer can separate out the colours shown in a flame to produce a spectrum of light emitted by each metal cation. A metal cation in an unknown solution can be identified by matching its spectrum to the spectrum from a known metal cation.

Other metal cations can be identified by adding **sodium hydroxide solution** to form a precipitate of the metal hydroxide:

- Solutions of aluminium and calcium ions form white precipitates but only the aluminium hydroxide precipitate dissolves in excess sodium hydroxide solution.
- Copper(II) ions form a blue precipitate, iron(II) ions a green precipitate and iron(III) ions a brown precipitate.

> You need to **learn** the results of these tests.

- Ammonium ions form ammonia gas.

**1** The diagram shows some spectra for some metal ions.

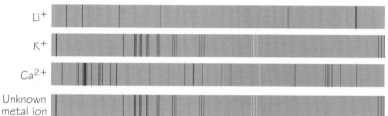

> Compare the spectra to find which one matches that of the unknown sample.

What is the metal ion in the unknown spectrum?  .................................................................................

**2** When sodium hydroxide solution is added to copper(II) sulfate solution, a precipitate forms.

**a** Complete the word equation:

copper(II) sulfate + sodium hydroxide → ........................................................ + sodium sulfate

**b** In the word equation above, circle Ⓐ the precipitate that forms.

**c** Why does a precipitate form? Tick ✓ **one** box.

The copper(II) cation reacts with a hydroxide anion to form a soluble compound.

The copper(II) hydroxide formed is insoluble.

The copper(II) hydroxide formed is less reactive than sodium hydroxide.

**3** Complete the sentences below to describe how to distinguish between an iron(II) sulfate solution and an iron(III) sulfate solution.

> Refer to the colours of precipitates above.

Both solutions contain the ................................. ion, but different cations. To distinguish between

the cations, add some ............................. solution, which produces a ............................................

precipitate in iron(II) sulfate solution and a ................................. precipitate in iron(III) sulfate.

**4** In the reaction in **3** the positive metal cations in solution react with the negative hydroxide ions in the sodium hydroxide solution. An insoluble metal hydroxide forms as a precipitate.

Complete the ionic equations for the reactions.

> Check that they balance.

$Fe^{2+}(aq) + 2OH^-(aq) \rightarrow Fe(OH)_2$ ....................

$Fe^{3+}(aq) + $ ................. $OH^-(aq) \rightarrow Fe(OH)_3(s)$

**2** **How can I identify the anions present in a compound?**

To identify the anions present in a compound, you need to learn the following tests.

| | Carbonate ion | Halide ion | Sulfate ion |
|---|---|---|---|
| Test | Add dilute hydrochloric acid | To the solution, add dilute nitric acid followed by silver nitrate solution | To the solution, add dilute hydrochloric acid followed by barium chloride solution |
| Result | Bubbles of carbon dioxide gas | White precipitate for chloride Cream precipitate for bromide Yellow precipitate for iodide | White precipitate |

**1** In the carbonate ion test, the gas produced must be tested to confirm it is carbon dioxide.

**a** Complete 🖉 these sentences.

> To confirm the gas produced is carbon dioxide it is bubbled into limewater. The
>
> limewater changes from ................................................. to ................................................. .

**b** Look at the halide and sulfate ion tests in the table above. The first step is to add acid to remove any carbonate ions present in the sample tested. If the carbonate ions remain, they would react in the second part of the test as shown by the ionic equations:

$2Ag^+(aq) + CO_3{}^{2-}(aq) \rightarrow Ag_2CO_3(s)$     $Ba^{2+}(aq) + CO_3{}^{2-}(aq) \rightarrow BaCO_3(s)$

Complete 🖉 these sentences.

> When silver nitrate is added to carbonate ions ................................................................. is
>
> formed. It is insoluble and so a white precipitate forms. When barium chloride is added to
>
> carbonate ions ................................................. is formed. It is insoluble and so a white
>
> ................................................. forms. Carbonate ions will therefore give a false positive test
>
> for sulfate and halide ions. Carbonate ions must be removed by adding ................................. .

**2** In the sulfate ion test, the negative sulfate ions react with the positive barium ions in the barium chloride solution. Insoluble barium sulfate forms as a white precipitate.

**a** Complete 🖉 the ionic equation for this reaction. Include the state symbols.

$Ba^{2+}(aq) + $ ...................... (.................) $\rightarrow$ ...................... (.................)

**b** Acids contain a hydrogen cation and an anion. Complete 🖉 the table.

| | Hydrochloric acid (HCl) | Nitric acid (HNO$_3$) | Sulfuric acid (H$_2$SO$_4$) |
|---|---|---|---|
| Anion present | chloride Cl$^-$ | | |

**c** Suggest 🖉 a reason that explains why dilute sulfuric acid, $H_2SO_4$, is **not** used to acidify the sample when testing for sulfate ions.

What is the negative ion in sulfuric acid?

.......................................................................................................................................................

**3** Halide ions react with silver ions to form insoluble precipitates. Why is dilute nitric acid as well as silver nitrate added in the halide test? 🖉

.......................................................................................................................................................

.......................................................................................................................................................

**3**  How can I use chemical tests to identify the ions in unknown single ionic compounds?

To identify the ions present in an ionic compound, anion and cation tests can be carried out. Look at the steps in each question below.

**1** Describe the test used to distinguish between sodium bromide and sodium chloride.

**a** Identify the ions to test for. Circle (A) the ions that are different in the two compounds.

**b** Are the different ions cations or anions? (🖉) ............................................................

**c** What substance can be added to identify the two different ions? (🖉) ............................................................

**d** Describe the test by completing (🖉) the sentences below.   Use the tests on page 44 to help.

> If the salt to be tested is a solid, make a solution by dissolving a spatula of the solid
>
> in water. Place about $5\,cm^3$ of each solution into a test tube and add a few drops of
>
> ................................................. Then add a few drops of ................................................. A
>
> ................................................. precipitate should form in the sodium chloride solution and a
>
> ................................................. precipitate should form in the sodium bromide solution.

**2** Describe the test used to distinguish between potassium sulfate and potassium chloride.

**a** Identify the ions to test for. Circle (A) the ions that are different in the two compounds.

**b** Are the different ions cations or anions? (🖉) ............................................................

**c** Two tests are used as two different ions need to be identified. Tick (✓) the **two** tests used.

add dilute acid and test for carbon dioxide

a flame test

add dilute nitric acid followed by silver nitrate

add dilute hydrochloric acid followed by barium chloride

add sodium hydroxide solution until in excess

**Remember** A flame test and adding sodium hydroxide solution are **cation** tests.

**d** Write (🖉) the results expected for each ion in a positive test.

1 .................................................   2 .................................................

For results of the tests refer to page 44.

**3** On paper, describe the test used to distinguish between calcium sulfate and aluminium sulfate. Use these questions to help you.

**a** Identify the ions to test for. Circle (A) the ions that are different in the two compounds.

**b** Are the different ions cations or anions? (🖉) ............................................................

**c** Tick (✓) the correct statement below.

A flame test will identify these two substances

Adding sodium hydroxide solution will identify the two substances

Adding sodium hydroxide solution in excess will identify the two substances

# Sample response

When describing how to test for ions in an ionic compound, both anion and cation tests are needed.

- **Cation** tests involve adding sodium hydroxide solution, using a flame test, or using flame photometry to produce a spectrum.
- **Anion** tests include:

  carbonate: adding dilute acid and testing for carbon dioxide gas
  halide: adding dilute nitric acid then silver nitrate solution (chloride, white precipitate; bromide, cream precipitate; iodide, yellow precipitate)
  sulfate: adding dilute hydrochloric acid then barium chloride solution (white precipitate).

Look at this exam-style question, and the sample response.

**Exam-style question**

1   A student carried out some tests to prove that a powder was aluminium chloride.

   Describe how the student carried out the tests. State the results obtained.

Here is a sample student answer.

First a spatula of the powder is dissolved in water to form a solution. Some of the solution is placed in a test tube and a few drops of sodium hydroxide solution is added. A white precipitate is formed. To confirm aluminium ions are present, excess sodium hydroxide solution is added and the white precipitate dissolves to form a colourless solution.

Some of the solution was placed in a different test tube and a few drops of nitric acid added, followed by silver nitrate solution. A white precipitate formed proving that chloride ions are present in the powder.

This is a comprehensive answer which fully explains how to prove the powder was aluminium chloride.

The powder is dissolved in water to form a solution because most ion tests are precipitation reactions which occur in solution.

(1) The student divided the answer into two parts, giving a test for aluminium ions first.

  a  Sodium hydroxide is added until it is in excess. Why is adding excess necessary to confirm aluminium ions?

Look at the results of the sodium hydroxide test on page 43.

.................................................................................................

.................................................................................................

  b  What is the name of the precipitate produced?  ...................................................

  c  Complete  the ionic equation for the formation of the precipitate.

$Al^{3+}(aq)$ + ........................... (aq) → ........................... (s)

(2) The student then described the test for chloride ions.

What might the nitric acid react with ?

  a  Why was adding nitric acid a necessary step in the test?

.................................................................................................

  b  Why does a white precipitate form when silver nitrate is added?

.................................................................................................

  c  Write an ionic equation with state symbols for the chloride ion test.

................... (...............) + ................... (...............) → ................... (...............)

Silver ions in the silver nitrate solution react with chloride ions.

# Your turn!

It is now time to use what you have learned to answer the exam-style question from page 41. Remember to read the question thoroughly, looking for information that may help you. Make good use of your knowledge from other areas of chemistry.

## Exam-style question

1   A student investigated three solutions.

    The solutions were aluminium chloride, calcium carbonate and iron(II) sulfate.

    (a)   The student carried out two tests. The results are shown in Figure 1.
          Complete Figure 1.                                                          **(3 marks)**

> To help you answer this you must learn the tests on page 44.

| Test | Aluminium chloride solution | Calcium carbonate solution | Iron(II) sulfate solution |
|---|---|---|---|
| adding dilute nitric acid followed by silver nitrate | | no change | no change |
| adding dilute hydrochloric acid followed by barium chloride | | | white precipitate |

Figure 1

    (b)   Explain why the student added dilute acid in each of the tests.          **(1 mark)**

          ............................................................................

          ............................................................................

> Barium carbonate and silver carbonate are insoluble.

    (c)   Write an ionic equation for the reaction between barium ions and sulfate ions. Include state symbols.          **(3 marks)**

> The reaction takes place in solution and produces a precipitate.

          ............................................................................

    (d)   In another experiment to identify the metal ion present in each solution, the student carried out flame tests and added sodium hydroxide solution to the metal ion solutions. The results of the tests are shown in Figure 2.          **(5 marks)**

          Complete Figure 2.

> To help you answer this you need to learn the tests given on page 43.

| | Aluminium chloride | Calcium carbonate | Iron(II) sulfate |
|---|---|---|---|
| flame test | no colour | | no colour |
| adding sodium hydroxide solution | | white precipitate | |
| adding excess sodium hydroxide solution | | | no change |

Figure 2

> **Remember** You only use a flame test to identify calcium, copper, lithium, potassium and sodium ions.

# Need more practice?

Questions about chemical analysis could occur as part of a question on, for example, salts, pure substances or an experiment, or as stand-alone questions.

Have a go at these exam-style questions. Write ✏ your answers to **2** and **3** on paper.

## Exam-style questions

1   Some ion tests were carried out on compounds **A**, **B** and **C**. The results are shown in Figure 1.

    Name compounds **A**, **B** and **C**.

To name the compounds you need to identify first the cation, using the flame test and sodium hydroxide results, and then the anion, using the silver nitrate and barium chloride results.

| | Flame test | Add sodium hydroxide solution | Add nitric acid and silver nitrate solution | Add hydrochloric acid and barium chloride solution |
|---|---|---|---|---|
| A | lilac flame | no reaction | yellow precipitate | no change |
| B | yellow flame | no reaction | no reaction | white precipitate |
| C | no flame | brown precipitate | white precipitate | no change |

Figure 1                                                                 (3 marks)

A ...................................   B ...................................   C ...................................

.................................   .................................   .................................

2   Explain why flame photometry would be used instead of flame tests to identify the metal ions in a mixture of lithium chloride and calcium sulfate.                    **(4 marks)**

3   Solid X is thought to be an aluminium or magnesium halide. A student carried out an experiment to determine if solid X contains aluminium or magnesium ions and to identify the halide ion present.

Halide ions include chloride, bromide and iodide.

To determine if the cation is aluminium or magnesium, is a flame test suitable or adding sodium hydroxide until in excess?

    Describe the experiment.
    Give the results for a positive test.                                    **(5 marks)**

## Boost your grade

To improve your grade make sure you:
• practise writing symbol and ionic equations for the reactions involved in ion tests
• learn how flame emission spectroscopy can also be used to identify metal ions in solution.

How confident do you feel about each of these **skills**? Colour in ✏ the bars.

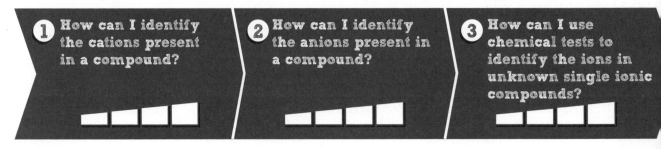

**1** How can I identify the cations present in a compound?

**2** How can I identify the anions present in a compound?

**3** How can I use chemical tests to identify the ions in unknown single ionic compounds?

# 7 Titrations

This unit will help you to understand how to carry out a titration. It will also help you to use the results to calculate the concentration of a solution.

In the exam, you will be asked to answer questions describing the method of titration. You will also have to calculate the mean volume of solutions used and the concentration of a solution.

## Exam-style question

1   A student added 25.0 cm$^3$ of sulfuric acid of unknown concentration to a conical flask.

The student carried out a titration to find out the volume of 0.200 mol dm$^{-3}$ sodium hydroxide needed to neutralise the sulfuric acid.

$$2NaOH + H_2SO_4 \rightarrow Na_2SO_4 + 2H_2O$$

(a)   What measuring instrument should the student use to measure out 25.0 cm$^3$ of sodium hydroxide solution? **(1 mark)**

(b)   Describe how the student would complete the titration.

You should name a suitable indicator and give the observed colour change.     **(4 marks)**

The student carried out three titrations. Her results are shown in Figure 1.

|                                    | Titration 1 | Titration 2 | Titration 3 |
|------------------------------------|-------------|-------------|-------------|
| Final burette reading (cm$^3$)     | 26.7        | 26.40       | 26.50       |
| Initial burette reading (cm$^3$)   | 0.00        | 0.20        | 0.40        |
| Volume of alkali used (cm$^3$)     | 26.7        | 26.20       | 26.10       |

Figure 1

(c)   Concordant results are within 0.10 cm$^3$ of each other.

Use the student's concordant results to calculate the mean volume of 0.200 mol dm$^{-3}$ sodium hydroxide solution added.     **(2 marks)**

(d)   Calculate the concentration of the sulfuric acid.

Give your answer in mol dm$^{-3}$ to three significant figures.     **(4 marks)**

You will already have done some work on titrations. Before starting the **skills boosts**, rate your confidence for each skill. Colour in 🖉 the bars.

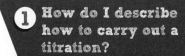

**1** How do I describe how to carry out a titration?

**2** How can I interpret the results from a titration?

**3** How do I calculate the concentration of a solution using results from a titration?

Titrations are used to determine the exact volume of one solution of known concentration, which reacts with a fixed volume of another solution of unknown concentration. The results can be used to find the concentration of a solution.

(1) A titration is usually carried out between an acid and an alkali.

   (a) Fill in 🖋 the missing parts of the general equation.

      acid + alkali → ................................................ + ................................................

   (b) i  Complete 🖋 the names of the salts of each acid in the list below.

      ii  Draw 🖋 lines to link each acid to its formula.

| Salt | Acid | Formula |
|------|------|---------|
| | hydrochloric acid | $HNO_3$ |
| nitrate | nitric acid | $H_2SO_4$ |
| | sulfuric acid | HCl |

> Look at the elements in the formula to help you deduce the name of the acid.

   (c) Complete 🖋 the word equations.

> sodium hydroxide + hydrochloric acid → ............................................. + water
>
> potassium hydroxide + ............................................. → potassium sulfate + .........................
>
> nitric acid + calcium hydroxide → ............................................. + .........................

(2) In a titration, a known volume of one solution is placed in a conical flask. This is done using a pipette with a safety filler. A few drops of indicator are added. The other solution is added from a burette until the indicator changes colour permanently. The volume added is recorded.

   (a) The diagram shows the apparatus used to carry out a titration of sodium hydroxide with hydrochloric acid. Write 🖋 labels on the diagram.

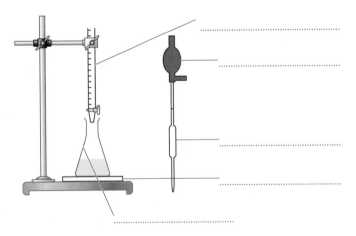

> A measuring cylinder measures out to the nearest $cm^3$. A pipette can measure out accurately to one decimal place, so it is used to measure out the solution used in a titration.

   (b) Why is a white tile used? Tick ✓ **one** box.

     A  To support the conical flask.

     B  To help you to see the colour change of the indicator more easily.

     C  To stop any spills from the burette falling on the bench.

**How do I describe how to carry out a titration?**

There are three different stages that must be mentioned when describing how to carry out a titration: filling the burette, adding an exact volume of solution to the conical flask, and adding the solution from the burette to the solution in the conical flask until there is a colour change shown by a suitable indicator.

This is the method for preparing a burette for titration.

**Step 1:** Fill the burette with the solution. Make sure that the jet is filled and that there are no air bubbles.

**Step 2:** Record the initial volume in the burette.

① Complete ✎ the sentences by circling the correct words.

> A meniscus is a **curved / straight** surface at the top of a column of liquid. When reading a burette volume, always read to the **top / bottom** of the meniscus at **head / eye** level. The reading on this burette is **22.0 / 22.1** cm³.

meniscus

Note that a burette has the measure 0.0 cm³ at the top and you read **downwards.**

② These are the steps to add an exact volume of solution (25.0 cm³) to the conical flask. Write ✎ numbers in the boxes to show the order in which you would carry out the steps.

☐ Place the flask under the burette on a white tile.

☐ Using a pipette filler, fill the pipette with 25.0 cm³ of solution.

☐ Release the solution into a conical flask.

☐ Add a few drops of an indicator, such as methyl orange or phenolphthalein.

③ During a titration, a student added a solution from the burette. The student swirled the contents of the conical flask until the indicator almost changed colour. The solution was then added slowly in drops. The volume of the solution added was recorded. This is called the **end point**.

**a** How could the student ensure that the result is reliable? ✎

............................................................................................

............................................................................................

For data to be reliable, similar results with little variation are obtained each time the experiment is repeated.

............................................................................................

**b** Why was the flask swirled? ✎

What happens to the solutions when the flask is swirled?

............................................................................................

④ A summary of the titration method used to find the concentration of hydrochloric acid is given below.

Complete ✎ the method by circling the correct words.

An alkali must be added to react with the hydrochloric acid.

> 25.0 cm³ of hydrochloric acid was placed in a **beaker / conical flask** using a **burette / pipette**. Three drops of indicator were added and the flask placed on a **stand / white tile**. Sodium **hydroxide / hydrochloric acid** was added from a **burette / pipette** with swirling until the indicator **disappeared / changed colour** permanently. The burette volume was recorded.

## 2 How can I interpret the results from a titration?

Titration results should be recorded in a table. When the burette is filled, the reading is taken and recorded as the initial burette reading. The solution is added to the conical flask until the colour of the indicator changes. At this stage, the reading on the burette is recorded as the final burette reading. All burette readings should be recorded to at least one decimal place. Repeat titrations should be carried out and the mean volume of solution added calculated.

**1** A student placed 25.0 cm³ of potassium hydroxide solution in a conical flask using a pipette and titrated with 0.200 mol dm⁻³ sulfuric acid. The student carried out five titrations. The volumes of 0.200 mol dm⁻³ sulfuric acid used in each titration were recorded in the table below.

**a** Circle Ⓐ the concordant results in the table below.

Concordant results are within 0.1 cm³ of each other.

| | Titration 1 | Titration 2 | Titration 3 | Titration 4 | Titration 5 |
|---|---|---|---|---|---|
| Volume of 0.200 mol dm⁻³ sulfuric acid | 12.80 | 12.50 | 12.45 | 12.40 | 12.65 |

**b** The first titration result is usually higher than the others. Why do you think this is? ✎

..............................................................................................................................................

..............................................................................................................................................

**2** A student placed 25.0 cm³ of sodium hydroxide solution in a conical flask and titrated with 0.100 mol dm⁻³ hydrochloric acid. The results were recorded in the table below.

| | Titration 1 | Titration 2 | Titration 3 | Titration 4 |
|---|---|---|---|---|
| Final burette reading (cm³) | 25.80 | 26.50 | 25.80 | 27.40 |
| Initial burette reading (cm³) | 0.00 | 1.20 | 0.40 | 1.95 |
| Volume of acid used (cm³) | 25.80 | 25.40 | | |

**a** Calculate the volumes of acid used in titrations 3 and 4 and fill in ✎ the missing values.

**b** In a titration, concordant results are used to calculate the mean volume of acid used. Concordant results are within 0.1 cm³ of each other. Circle Ⓐ the concordant results.

**c** Use the concordant results to calculate ✎ the mean volume of acid used in the titration.

To find the mean, add the results together and divide by the total number of results used.

**d** Methyl orange indicator was used in this titration. Methyl orange indicator is red in acid and yellow in alkali. Give the colour change at the end point.

Sodium hydroxide is an alkali.

..............................................................................................................................................

**3** Which of the statements below will help to ensure that accurate results are obtained when carrying out this titration? Tick ✓ all the correct boxes.

**A** Use a burette to measure the volume of acid. ☐

**B** Use a pipette to measure the volume of sodium hydroxide. ☐

**C** Swirl the flask during the titration. ☐

**D** Add the acid drop by drop at the end point. ☐

**E** Use a burette to add the acid as quickly as possible. ☐

**F** Use a pipette filler. ☐

**3** **How do I calculate the concentration of a solution using results from a titration?**

To calculate the concentration of a solution by titration, break the calculation into steps:
- **Calculate the number of moles** from the concentration and volume.
- **Determine the ratio of the reactants** from the balanced symbol equation and use it to find the number of moles of the reacting substance.
- **Calculate the concentration** of the substance using the moles and the volume.

**Exam-style question**

1   A student used a pipette to add 25.0 cm³ of sodium hydroxide solution of unknown concentration to a conical flask.

The student carried out a titration against 0.400 mol dm⁻³ sulfuric acid.

The equation for this reaction is: $2NaOH + H_2SO_4 \rightarrow Na_2SO_4 + 2H_2O$

The average volume of sulfuric acid needed for complete neutralisation was 19.60 cm³.

Calculate the concentration of the sodium hydroxide.

Give your answer to three significant figures.

**①** **a** Complete ✎ the sentence for the first step in the calculation.

I can calculate the number of moles of **sulfuric acid** because I know two pieces of information:

the volume, ........................................, and the ........................................, 0.400 mol dm⁻³.

**b** Write ✎ the missing information in the equation below to calculate the number of moles.

> To convert cm³ to dm³ divide by 1000.

$$\text{moles of } H_2SO_4 = \frac{\text{volume (cm}^3)}{1000} \times \text{concentration (mol dm}^{-3}) = \frac{19.60}{1000} \times \text{........................} = 0.00784$$

**Use the mole ratio** in the balanced symbol equation to work out the number of moles of the other substance reacting (sodium hydroxide).

> The mole ratio is given by the balancing numbers in the equation. If there is no number, this means 1 mole.

The equation is $2NaOH + H_2SO_4 \rightarrow Na_2SO_4 + 2H_2O$.
The mole ratio is $H_2SO_4 : 2NaOH$

**②** Complete ✎ the sentences below.

> The mole ratio shows there are twice as many moles of NaOH as $H_2SO_4$, so multiply the moles of $H_2SO_4$ by 2 to get the moles of NaOH.

........................ mole of $H_2SO_4$ reacts with 2 moles of NaOH

0.00784 mole of $H_2SO_4$ reacts with ........................ moles of NaOH

**③** Write ✎ the missing values in the equation below to calculate the concentration.

> To convert dm³ to cm³ multiply by 1000.

$$\text{concentration of NaOH} \atop (\text{mol dm}^{-3}) = 1000 \times \frac{\text{moles of NaOH}}{\text{volume (cm}^3)} = 1000 \times \frac{\boxed{\phantom{xxxx}}}{25.0} = \text{........................}$$

In a titration calculation, always carry out the three steps in order: **calculate moles, determine and use the mole ratio, calculate concentration.**

> Give your answer to three significant figures. The first significant figure is always the first non-zero digit from the left. If the fourth figure is 5 or more, then round up.

# Sample response

When describing a titration, remember to describe the three stages mentioned on page 51. You can calculate the unknown concentration using the steps on page 53.

Exam-style question

1  (a)  Describe how a student could carry out a titration to determine the volume of $0.100\,mol\,dm^{-3}$ potassium hydroxide that is needed to react with $25.0\,cm^3$ of sulfuric acid of unknown concentration.

Look at this student's answer and use the questions below to help you think about how to improve it.

*$25.0\,cm^3$ of sulfuric acid solution of unknown concentration was measured out using a measuring cylinder and added to a conical flask. Three drops of phenolphthalein indicator were added. The burette was filled with $0.100\,mol\,dm^{-3}$ potassium hydroxide and checked. The initial burette reading was recorded and the alkali added until the indicator changed colour. The experiment was repeated.*

① a  How should the $25.0\,cm^3$ be measured out accurately? 🖉 ..........................................

..........................................................................................................................

b  What should the student check when filling the burette? 🖉 ..........................................

..........................................................................................................................

c  How should the student read the meniscus? 🖉 ..........................................

d  How could the solution be added more accurately at the end point? 🖉 ..........................................

..........................................................................................................................

Exam-style question

1  (b)  The average volume of potassium hydroxide needed for complete neutralisation was $22.50\,cm^3$. The equation for the reaction is: $2KOH + H_2SO_4 \rightarrow K_2SO_4 + 2H_2O$

Calculate the concentration of the sulfuric acid in $mol\,dm^{-3}$.

Look at the student's answer.

$$\text{moles of KOH} = \frac{\text{volume } (cm^3)}{1000} \times \text{conc } (mol\,dm^{-3}) = \frac{25.0}{1000} \times 0.100 = 0.0025$$

② a  Circle Ⓐ the error in the first step of the student's answer.

b  Calculate 🖉 the concentration of the sulfuric acid:

$$\text{moles of KOH} = \frac{\text{volume } (cm^3)}{1000} \times \text{conc } (mol\,dm^{-3}) = \frac{\boxed{\phantom{xxx}}}{1000} \times \text{..............} = \text{..............}$$

c  Calculate 🖉 the actual number of moles of $H_2SO_4$ that react with $0.00225$ moles KOH using the mole ratio $H_2SO_4 : 2KOH$.

1 mole of $H_2SO_4$ reacts with 2 moles of KOH

.......................... moles of $H_2SO_4$ react with $0.00225$ moles of KOH

> The number of moles of $H_2SO_4$ is half the number of moles of KOH, so divide the number of moles of KOH by 2 to get the number of moles of $H_2SO_4$.

d  Complete 🖉 the calculation to determine the concentration of $H_2SO_4$.

$$\frac{\text{concentration}}{\text{of } H_2SO_4\ (mol\,dm^{-3})} = \frac{1000 \times \text{moles of KOH}}{\text{volume } (cm^3)} = \frac{1000 \times \boxed{\phantom{xxx}}}{25.0} = \text{..............}$$

# Your turn!

It is now time to use what you have learned to answer the exam-style question from page 49. Remember to read the question thoroughly, looking for information that may help you. Make good use of your knowledge from other areas of chemistry.

Write ✏️ your answer to (d) on paper.

## Exam-style question

1   A student added 25.0 cm³ of sulfuric acid of unknown concentration to a conical flask.

The student carried out a titration to find out the volume of 0.200 mol dm⁻³ sodium hydroxide needed to neutralise the sulfuric acid.

$$2NaOH + H_2SO_4 \rightarrow Na_2SO_4 + 2H_2O$$

(a)  What measuring instrument should the student use to measure out 25.0 cm³ of sulfuric acid?                                                                                 (1 mark)

........................................................................................................................................

(b)  Describe how the student would complete the titration.

You should name a suitable indicator and give the observed colour change.          (4 marks)

.............................................................................

.............................................................................

.............................................................................          The acid is in the conical flask so the starting colour of the indicator in this titration will be its colour in acid solution.

.............................................................................

.............................................................................

.............................................................................

.............................................................................

The student carried out three titrations. Her results are shown in Figure 1.

|                                     | Titration 1 | Titration 2 | Titration 3 |
| ----------------------------------- | ----------- | ----------- | ----------- |
| Final burette reading (cm³)         | 26.70       | 26.40       | 26.50       |
| Initial burette reading (cm³)       | 0.00        | 0.20        | 0.40        |
| Volume of alkali used (cm³)         | 26.7        | 26.20       | 26.10       |

Figure 1

(c)  Concordant results are within 0.10 cm³ of each other. Use the student's concordant results to calculate the mean volume of 0.200 mol dm⁻³ sodium hydroxide solution added.          (2 marks)

To calculate the mean, add the concordant results together and divide by the total number of concordant results.

(d)  Calculate the concentration of the sulfuric acid.          **Remember** Follow through the steps: calculate moles, use the mole ratio, calculate concentration.

Give your answer in mol dm⁻³ to three significant figures.          (4 marks)

# Need more practice?

Questions about titrations could occur as part of a question on different types of calculation, part of a question about an experiment or investigation, or as stand-alone questions.

Have a go at this exam-style question.

## Exam-style question

1   In a titration, a student added 25.0 cm³ of sodium hydroxide solution to a conical flask. The student then added three drops of an indicator.

The student added sulfuric acid from a burette until there was a colour change. The end point required 22.5 cm³ of a 0.500 mol dm⁻³ solution of sulfuric acid.

The equation for the reaction is: $2NaOH + H_2SO_4 \rightarrow Na_2SO_4 + 2H_2O$

(a)   Name a suitable indicator for this titration.                                                        (1 mark)

........................................................................................................................................................

(b)   State the colour change at the end point for the indicator you have chosen.          (1 mark)

........................................................................................................................................................

(c)   Describe how the student measured 25.0 cm³ of sodium hydroxide solution accurately and placed it in the conical flask.                                                                (2 marks)

........................................................................................................................................................

........................................................................................................................................................

(d)   Calculate the concentration of the sodium hydroxide solution in mol dm⁻³.          (4 marks)

Give your answer to three significant figures.

concentration = ............................... mol dm⁻³

## Boost your grade

To improve your grade, make sure you can convert concentration in mol dm⁻³ to concentration in g dm⁻³ by multiplying by the relative formula mass (M). You should also practise titration calculations where you are asked to calculate the volume of a solution reacting.

How confident do you feel about each of these **skills**? Colour in  the bars.

1  **How do I describe how to carry out a titration?**

2  **How can I interpret the results from a titration?**

3  **How do I calculate the concentration of a solution using results from a titration?**

# ⑧ Answering questions about practicals

This unit will help you to answer questions based on practical work and practical situations.

In the exam, you will be asked to answer questions such as the one below.

**Exam-style question**

1   A student investigated the electrolysis of copper chloride solution using the apparatus shown in Figure 1.

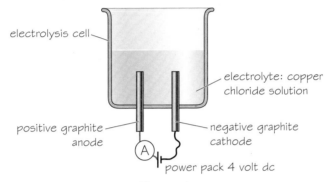

Figure 1

(a)   Predict the product formed at the anode.                                                     **(1 mark)**

(b)   Describe a simple laboratory test that you could carry out to test your prediction for the anode.                                                                                      **(2 marks)**

(c)   The student investigated how the mass of copper formed at the cathode changed when the current was increased.

    (i)    Write a balanced half equation for the reaction at the cathode.            **(1 mark)**

    (ii)   Describe **two** measurements which the student should make.            **(2 marks)**

    (iii)  Give **two** variables that the student should control to make the investigation a fair test.                                                                        **(2 marks)**

    (iv)   Describe how the student could ensure that the results are valid.        **(2 marks)**

You will already have done some practical work. Before starting the **skills boosts**, rate your confidence in answering questions about practicals. Colour in 🖉 the bars.

| **①** How do I describe a suitable experiment? | **②** How do I change an investigation? | **③** How do I improve the validity of results? |
| --- | --- | --- |

Scientists form a hypothesis, using their chemical understanding, knowledge and observations from previous experiments. They then design suitable experiments to test the hypothesis.

Many variables may affect the results of an experiment. So when designing a suitable experiment you must describe clearly how all these variables will be altered, measured or kept constant. It is important to make sure that the results are repeatable and reproducible so that a valid conclusion can be made.

(1) Draw ✐ lines to match the key words to their meaning. One has already been done for you.

| Key word | Meaning |
|---|---|
| variable | a proposal intended to explain certain facts or observations |
| control variable | a chemical quantity or characteristic that can be changed |
| independent variable | this is what you measure |
| dependent variable | this is changed during the investigation |
| hypothesis | a conclusion based on data from an appropriate experiment |
| repeatable | the same results obtained from another person or technique |
| reproducible | the same results obtained when the experiment is repeated |
| valid conclusion | this must be kept constant during the investigation |

(2) **a** Circle Ⓐ the independent variable in each of the following experiments.

**b** Highlight ✐ the dependent variable in each of the following experiments.

A   An investigation into the effect of different catalysts on the time taken to produce 10 cm³ of oxygen during the decomposition of hydrogen peroxide.

B   The effect of different acid concentrations on the temperature changes that take place during a neutralisation reaction.

> Ask yourself the questions.
> 'What is being changed?'
> 'What is being measured?'

C   The effect of different mobile phase on the position of spots seen on a chromatogram.

(3) The difference between the maximum and minimum values of the independent or dependent variable is known as the range. The size of the range is important when looking for patterns in the data.

| Temperature (°C) | Time (s) |
|---|---|
| 20 | 267 |
| 40 | 20 |
| 45 | 10 |

The table shows some experimental data obtained when a student investigated how temperature affects the rate of a reaction.

Complete the sentences by circling Ⓐ the correct word in each pair in **bold**.

> A valid conclusion **can / cannot** be made from this data because the
>
> temperature range is too **small / large**.
>
> At each temperature the student recorded **one data point / three data**
>
> **points**, so it is **possible / not possible** to tell if the results are repeatable.

At least 4 or 5 data points are usually required to identify a pattern in the results.

**1** **How do I describe a suitable experiment?**

To describe a suitable experiment, you must:
- identify the independent, dependent and control variables
- use or develop a hypothesis based on your chemical knowledge or observations from previous experiments
- apply your chemical knowledge to plan an experiment to make observations and test the hypothesis.

**①** A student investigated the electrolysis of aqueous solutions of salts. She made a hypothesis based on an observation from a previous electrolysis experiment.

> During the electrolysis of copper sulfate solution, copper is deposited on the negative electrode. Increasing the current during the electrolysis will increase the mass of metal deposited on the negative electrode.

**a** Underline Ⓐ the hypothesis.

Next the student thought about the actual experiment that she would use to test her hypothesis. She made some notes to get started.

> A   Make up a solution of copper sulfate or copper chloride solution to test.
>
> B   Chlorine will displace iodine from a solution of iodide salts.
>
> C   In electrolysis, electricity is used to split up compounds, so we need to set up an electric circuit.
>
> D   Ammeters are used to measure current.
>
> E   Small test tubes can be used to collect any gas given off so we can test it.
>
> F   Graphite electrodes are inert.

**b** Highlight ✏ the notes that helped the student to design an experiment to test her hypothesis.

Make sure that you only use relevant ideas.

Finally the student set up the equipment shown in the diagram.

**c** Look at the diagram and then complete ✏ the table below. You must include at least **two** control variables.

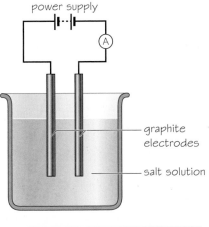

4 volt dc power supply

graphite electrodes

salt solution

Control variables are things that cannot be changed during the experiment

| Independent variable | |
|---|---|
| Dependent variable | |
| Control variables | |

**2** **How do I change an investigation?**

To change an investigation you need to identify the variables. Then change one variable and make sure that the rest are controlled. Decide on the range and collect some data.

You can widen the range in an investigation to confirm a pattern in some data. You can also carry out further tests to support or disprove your conclusion.

**1** A student investigated the electrolysis of aqueous solutions of salts. His results from previous experiments are shown in the table below.

| Salt solution | Observation at the anode (+) | Possible product at anode | Observation at the cathode (−) | Possible product at cathode |
|---|---|---|---|---|
| Copper sulfate | colourless bubbles | oxygen | brown solid on electrode | copper |
| Lead nitrate | colourless bubbles | oxygen | grey solid on electrode | lead |
| Sodium chloride | chlorine smell | chlorine | colourless bubbles | hydrogen |

Based on his chemical knowledge, the student made some predictions about his observations. He also carried out some further tests. His final conclusions are written below.

> At the anode, negative ions lose electrons. So the colourless bubbles seen at the anode are oxygen gas. At the cathode, positive ions gain electrons. So the solids are copper and lead and the colourless bubbles seen at the cathode are hydrogen gas.

**a** The student wanted to continue the investigation to answer the following question: When a copper salt is electrolysed, is copper always produced at the cathode?

Here are two possible investigations that could help answer his question.

> **A** The effect of changing the electric current on the mass of copper produced.
>
> **B** The effect of changing the copper salt on the products produced at the cathode.

  i Circle (A) the independent variable in **A** and **B**.

  ii Highlight (✏) the dependent variable.

  iii State (✏) what should be controlled.

   **A** Control variables: .......................................................................................................................

   **B** Control variables: .......................................................................................................................

  iv Underline (A) the investigation he should carry out to answer his question.

**b** The student then investigated the effect of changing the electric current on the mass of copper produced at the electrode. What range of current in amps (A), should he use? Tick (✓) **one** box.

| | | | |
|---|---|---|---|
| 0.2 | ☐ | 0.01–0.02 | ☐ |
| 0.1–0.5 | ☐ | 1 | ☐ |

The range is the difference between the maximum and minimum values of the independent or dependent variables.

**c** Give (✏) a reason for your answer. .......................................................................................................

..............................................................................................................................................................

**3**  **How do I improve the validity of results?**

The validity of results can be improved by ensuring that they are obtained by using a suitable procedure where variables are controlled, are accurate and precise, are repeatable and reproducible.

**(1)** Circle Ⓐ the correct words to complete the sentences.

> **Precise / Accurate** measurements are ones in which there is very little spread about the mean value. A result is considered to be **precise / accurate** if it is judged to be close to a true value.

**(2)** The diagram shows the results of a darts match. Each player was trying to get as close to the centre as they could. How would you describe each game?

Write 🖉 the correct letter in each box.

Precise and accurate

Not precise but accurate

Precise but not accurate

Not precise or accurate

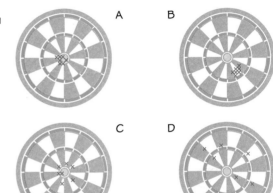

**(3)** The table shows the results of a copper sulfate electrolysis investigation carried out by two groups of students.

Group 1

| Current in amps (A) | 0.2 | 0.3 | 0.4 | 0.5 |
|---|---|---|---|---|
| Mass of cathode at start (g) | 2.77 | 2.68 | 2.53 | 2.36 |
| Mass of cathode at end (g) | 2.85 | 2.79 | 2.67 | 2.99 |
| Mass increase (g) | 0.08 | 0.11 | 0.14 | 0.63 |

Group 2

| Current in amps (A) | 0.2 | 0.3 | 0.4 | 0.5 |
|---|---|---|---|---|
| Mass of cathode at start (g) | 2.8 | 2.7 | 2.5 | 2.4 |
| Mass of cathode at end (g) | 2.9 | 2.7 | 2.7 | 2.6 |
| Mass increase (g) | 0.1 | 0.0 | 0.2 | 0.2 |

**a** Circle Ⓐ the anomalous result obtained by Group 1.

**b** Suggest 🖉 a reason why the result may be anomalous.

> Anomalous results do not follow any pattern observed in the results.

**c** The students in Group 1 think that they will improve the validity of the results if they repeat the experiments and calculate the mean result.
Explain 🖉 why they are correct.

> Scientists deal with anomalous results by repeating that part of the experiment, taking extra care, or not using these results when drawing their conclusions.
>
> To calculate the mean, add up all the results and divide by the total number of results.

**d** Circle Ⓐ the correct word to complete the sentences.

> The data obtained by Group 2 does not show the same pattern as that obtained by Group 1. So the results are not **reproducible / repeatable.** This may be due to using a balance with a **low / high** resolution that only measures to **one decimal place / two decimal places.**

> The resolution of a measuring instrument is the smallest change in the quantity being measured, e.g. 1 g, 0.1 g or 0.01 g.

# Sample response

Here is an exam-style question about rates of reaction. Use the student responses to this question to improve your answers to questions about designing experiments, identifying and controlling variables and improving the validity of results.

## Exam-style question

1   Two students monitored the progress of a reaction at different temperatures by observing the time taken for a colour change to obscure their view of a cross drawn on paper. Their results were recorded in the tables below.

### Student A

| Mean temperature (°C) | Time taken for cross to disappear (s) |
|---|---|
| 20 | 164 |
| 30 | 78 |
| 40 | 45 |
| 45 | 20 |

### Student B

| Mean temperature (°C) | Time taken for cross to disappear (s) | | | Mean time taken (s) |
|---|---|---|---|---|
| | Trial 1 | Trial 2 | Trial 3 | |
| 20.1 | 165 | 175 | 165 | 165 |
| 30.2 | 82 | 83 | 81 | 82 |
| 40.0 | 42 | 42 | 42 | 42 |
| 45.0 | 21 | 20 | 22 | 21 |

Suggest reasons why the results produced by student B are likely to be more valid than those produced by student A.

(3 marks)

Here is one student's answer.

> Student A only carried out each experiment once whereas student B did each one three times and took the average. So the data recorded by student B is repeatable. We can't tell if the results produced by student A are repeatable.

(1)  To improve this answer the student needs also to consider anomalous results.

An anomalous result is one where the difference between it and the other values is much greater than the difference between the other values.

a   Are any of the results produced by student A anomalous?

.................................................................................................................................

b   What advice would you give to student A?

.................................................................................................................................

c   Why did student B leave data point 175 out when calculating the mean time taken at 20.1 °C?

.................................................................................................................................

d   Why do anomalous results occur?

.................................................................................................................................

.................................................................................................................................

.................................................................................................................................

# Your turn!

It is now time to use what you have learned to answer the exam-style question from page 57. Remember to read the question thoroughly, looking for information that may help you. Make good use of your knowledge from other areas of chemistry.

## Exam-style question

1   A student investigated the electrolysis of copper chloride solution using the apparatus shown in Figure 1.

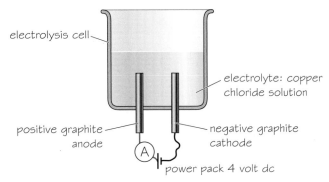

electrolysis cell

electrolyte: copper chloride solution

positive graphite anode

negative graphite cathode

A

power pack 4 volt dc

**Figure 1**

(a)  Predict the product formed at the anode. ........................................................................... (1 mark)

(b)  Describe a simple laboratory test that you could carry out to test your prediction for the anode.                                                    (2 marks)

.................................................................................................................................................

.................................................................................................................................................

.................................................................................................................................................

(c)  The student investigated how the mass of copper formed at the cathode changed when the current was increased.

(i)   Write a balanced half equation for the reaction at the cathode.          (1 mark)

.................................................................................................................................................

(ii)  Describe **two** measurements which the student should make.          (2 marks)

.................................................................................................................................................

.................................................................................................................................................

(iii) Give **two** variables the student should control to make the investigation a fair test.                                                             (2 marks)

.................................................................................................................................................

.................................................................................................................................................

.................................................................................................................................................

(iv)  Describe how the student could ensure that the results are valid.       (2 marks)

.................................................................................................................................................

.................................................................................................................................................

.................................................................................................................................................

# Need more practice?

Questions on this topic could occur as questions about experiments or investigations only or as part of a question on most chemistry topics.

You may be asked to:

- describe or design an experiment
- suggest ways to improve validity of the results by collecting further evidence or extending the investigation
- evaluate the quality of the data.

Have a go at these exam-style questions. Write 🖊 your answer to **2** on paper.

## Exam-style questions

1  Sodium carbonate solution reacts with zinc chloride solution to produce the insoluble salt, zinc carbonate.

$$Na_2CO_3(aq) + ZnCl_2(aq) \rightarrow 2NaCl(aq) + ZnCO_3(s)$$

Describe how a pure, dry sample of zinc carbonate can be obtained. **(4 marks)**

2  Describe an experiment to produce a dry sample of potassium sulfate crystals. **(6 marks)**

Potassium hydroxide is an alkaline solution that can be used to produce a potassium salt.

Which acid produces sulfate salts?

Potassium sulfate is a soluble salt. You will need to think back to when you learnt about the preparation of soluble salts.

Use word or symbol equations to show your understanding of how to make a salt.

## Boost your grade

Make sure you are able to use and apply your practical skills to a range of different contexts.

How confident do you feel about each of these **skills**? Colour in 🖊 the bars.

**1** How do I describe a suitable experiment?

**2** How do I change an investigation?

**3** How do I improve the validity of results?

# ⑨ Answering extended response questions

This unit will help you to answer longer questions by deciding what is being asked, and then planning a concise answer with the right detail.

In the exam, you will be asked to answer questions such as the one below.

**Exam-style question**

1   Describe an experiment to produce a pure, dry sample of copper chloride crystals.   **(6 marks)**

You will already have done some work on this. Before starting the **skills boosts**, rate your confidence in each one. Colour in 🖉 the bars.

**①** **How do I know what the question is asking me to do?**

**②** **How do I plan my answer?**

**③** **How do I choose the right detail to answer the question concisely?**

A good answer to an extended response question has the ideas well organised, correctly linked and supported with relevant scientific evidence.

(1) Tick ✓ the statements that show the best way to answer an extended response question.

Write your ideas in any order. ☐

Link your ideas together to show understanding. ☐

Write everything you know about the topic even if it isn't relevant. ☐

Use correct scientific vocabulary. ☐

Write your answer in an ordered way. ☐

The first word in the question is usually the command word, which tells you what you need to do. The Edexcel website lists the command words you need to understand.

> **Give, describe, explain** and **predict** are common command words.

> **Predict** means to give the expected result.

The same question requires a different response depending on which command word is used.

(2) Draw 🖉 lines to join each question with the **two** responses that best match it.

**Question**

| Give two signs of a reaction that would be **seen** when a piece of sodium is dropped into a container of water. |

| Describe what would be **seen** when a piece of sodium is dropped into a container of water. |

| Explain what would be **seen** when a piece of sodium is dropped into a container of water. |

**Response**

| The metal moves around on the water rapidly because the reaction is very vigorous. |

| The metal moves around on the water rapidly. |

| The metal disappears. |

| Bubbles coming off where the sodium meets the water. |

| Bubbles. |

| Bubbles because hydrogen gas is given off. |

> **Describe** answers are likely to have more detail than **give** answers.

> **Explain** answers usually include the word 'because'.

**1    How do I know what the question is asking me to do?**

Follow these three steps to help you understand what the question is asking.

**Step 1:** Look at the command word.

**Step 2:** Look for anything else the question is asking you to do.

**Step 3:** Read the question carefully and think about all the information provided.

Read the exam-style question, then answer it using the three steps in ①, ② and ③ below.

**Exam-style question**

1   Figure 1 lists some experimental data about the reactions of metals.

Describe the relative reactivity of metals based on this experimental data.    **(6 marks)**

| Metal | Reaction with water | Reaction with hydrochloric acid |
|---|---|---|
| Copper | No change | No change |
| Lithium | Vigorous effervescence Colourless gas formed | Explosive reaction |
| Zinc | No change | Bubbles of colourless gas |
| Magnesium | A few bubbles form on surface of metal | Bubbles rapidly form on surface |

Figure 1

① **a** Circle Ⓐ the command word in the exam-style question.

**b** What is the command word telling you to do? 🖉

.........................................................................................................................................

② **a** The question asks you to describe the reactivity of metals. Highlight 🖉 the other key words in the question that tell you how to do this.

   **Relative** means 'compared to' in this context.

   In this question, you should only use evidence that is given to you, **not** other things you know.

**b** What are these words telling you to do? 🖉

.........................................................................................................................................

.........................................................................................................................................

**c** What information do you need to use to describe the relative reactivity? 🖉

   Re-read the exam-style question. You will find the answer there.

   You need to link the information provided to the question being asked.

.........................................................................................................................................

③ **a** What is the data in the table telling you? 🖉 ..........................................................................

.........................................................................................................................................

**b** Draw 🖉 a box around each data set.    **c** Highlight 🖉 the metals listed in the table.

**d** Write 🖉 the metals in order of increasing reactivity with

   **i** water: .........................................................................................................................

   **ii** hydrochloric acid: .......................................................................................................

**e** How do the reactions with hydrochloric acid help you with your final answer?

.........................................................................................................................................

.........................................................................................................................................

You can plan your answer by thinking about the topic as a whole, deciding which parts of the topic are relevant to the question, and structuring your answer by putting the points in a logical order. Use the questions below to help you plan your answer to the exam-style question.

You can use these general questions to plan a description of practical work.

| | |
|---|---|
| What is the chemical reaction? | Consider the variables involved in the reaction. What needs to be changed or controlled? |
| What reactants will you need? | |
| What equipment will you use? | What are the main steps in the method and what order should they be done in? |
| How will you use the equipment? | What precautions must you take? |
| What will you observe or measure? | Do you need to use any safety equipment? |
| How will you make it a fair test? | How will you record your results? |

**Exam-style question**

1   Describe an experiment to produce a pure, dry sample of copper sulfate crystals.
    Your method should be safe.

(6 marks)

Copper sulfate is a soluble salt. You may have made a different salt in your core practical so you will need to apply your knowledge of chemistry.

**(1)** Cross out ~~(the)~~ the general questions that are not relevant to making copper sulfate crystals.

Here you are making a sample of a salt and not carrying out a full investigation so considering the variables is not important at the planning stage.

Writing down the word or symbol equation is a good start because it can be used to begin the plan.

The question is asking you to **describe** the method so you do not need to include any results or explanations.

**(2)** Complete the chemical equation for the reaction:

copper oxide + sulfuric acid → copper sulfate + water

$CuO(s)$  +  $H_2SO_4(aq)$  →  ................(aq)  +  ................(l)

**(3)** **a**  What **three** things does the chemical equation tell you?

.........................................................................................................................................

**b**  Underline Ⓐ the general questions that the equation will help you to fully or partly answer.

Knowing the states of the reactants and products will help you work out what equipment is needed to measure out the reactants or collect the products.

You can now plan your answer by structuring your points in a logical order and writing some notes.

Use these steps:
1. chemical equation
2. steps in method
3. equipment needed for each step
4. risk assessment

## 3 How do I choose the right detail to answer the question concisely?

You can answer the question concisely by:

- following your plan and making sure that you are selecting the parts of the topic that **answer** the question, rather than attempting to write down everything you know about the topic
- referring back to the command word to see the key elements that you should use in your answer
- expressing your ideas as clearly and precisely as possible.

### Exam-style question

1 Figure 1 lists some data about the halogens.

| Halogen | Melting point (°C) | Density (kg m$^{-3}$) | Appearance | Effect of hot iron wool |
|---|---|---|---|---|
| Fluorine | −220 | 1.6 | Pale yellow gas | Bursts into flames |
| Chlorine | −101 | 3.2 | Green gas | Glows brightly |
| Bromine | −7 | 3120 | Brown liquid | Glows dull red |
| Iodine | 114 | 4950 | Purple/black solid | Changes colour |

Figure 1

Explain the relative reactivity of the halogens in terms of electronic structure. **(6 marks)**

(1) What is the difference between **explain** and **describe**? 🖉

..................................................................................................

..................................................................................................

> **Explain** means to make something clear, or state the reasons for something happening.

(2) In the exam-style question, highlight 🖉 the key scientific ideas the question is asking about.

(3) Read this student's notes on this topic and highlight 🖉 the relevant information.

> The reactivity of metals increases down the group.
> The reactivity of halogens decreases down the group.
> Non-metals share electrons during covalent bonding.
> The electronic structure is the way in which an atom's electrons are arranged.
> The electronic structure of chlorine is 2,8,7.
> As you go down the group the distance between the electron in the outer shell and the nucleus increases.
> During bonding, metals lose electrons to form positive ions.
> The formation of negative ions is important for reactivity.
> The force of attraction depends on distance from the nucleus.

> **Remember** In some exam questions you will have to rely on your own knowledge recall as you will not be given lots of information in the question. In the exam you will have a copy of the periodic table.

(4) Use your own knowledge to give any further information that you might need to answer the question. 🖉

..................................................................................................

..................................................................................................

..................................................................................................

> Include an example of the relative reactivity of the halogens. Look at the data listed in Figure 1 above.

**Unit 9 Answering extended response questions** 69

# Sample response

Use this sample student response to improve the way you answer these types of questions. Use information given in the unit to help you. Consider if the command word has been properly answered and all the points covered in an organised manner.

**Exam-style question**

1 Describe how a student could carry out an experiment to compare the reactivity of the metals copper, zinc and magnesium.

You have samples of the three metals and the metal sulfate solutions, and can use any classroom laboratory equipment. **(6 marks)**

Here is one student's answer.

Copper and zinc are transition metals. Magnesium is in group 2 and has 2 electrons on the outer electron shell. Copper is used to make electrical wires because it is a good conductor and also to make pipes to carry water.

Put a bit of the first metal into all three of the liquids and see what it does. Repeat for the other metals. Decide which one is the most reactive and draw a results table.

Word equation:

metal + METAL sulfate → METAL + metal sulfate

This is called a displacement reaction.

1 **a** Highlight 🖉 the command word.

**b** Cross out ~~cat~~ any irrelevant information in the student answer.

**c** Has the student given enough detail to answer the question? Ⓐ **Yes / No**

**d** Is the response written in an organised and logical way? Ⓐ **Yes / No**

Has the student included the following details?
- The variables involved
- The experimental method
- Any observations to compare the reactivities
- How they are going to decide which is the most reactive metal.

The question is asking you to describe **how** to do an experiment. You are not asked to predict or give the results, or to explain what is happening.

The reactivity of metals can be compared by finding out which metals will displace each other. When metal 1 is added to another metal sulfate solution, if metal 1 is more reactive than the one in the sulfate solution, a new metal sulfate will form and the other metal will be deposited out of the solution.

2 Now answer 🖉 the question yourself on paper.

- What equipment will you use and how will you use it?
- Consider the variables involved in the reaction. What needs to be changed or controlled?
- What will you observe or measure to compare the reactivity, and how will you record this?
- How will you decide the order of reactivity?
- How will you write this information in an ordered way?

# Your turn!

It is now time to use what you have learned to answer the exam-style question from page 65. Remember to read the question thoroughly, looking for information that may help you. Make good use of your knowledge from other areas of chemistry.

Read the exam-style question and answer it using the guided steps below.

**Exam-style question**

1   Describe an experiment to produce a pure, dry sample of copper chloride crystals.   **(6 marks)**

**1** **a** Highlight ✎ the command word in the question.

**b** What does the command word mean you need to do? ✎ ...................................................
.........................................................................................................................................

**c** Which acid produces chloride salts? ✎ ...........................................................................

Now think about the equipment you need and how you will use it, and also consider safety.

**d** Match the process to the equipment you will use by writing ✎ the correct letter in each box.

To show how you will use the equipment it is often helpful to draw some diagrams.

A          B          C          D

Heating the reactants  ☐

Filtering  ☐

Evaporation  ☐

Crystallisation  ☐

Plan your answer to get your steps in the right order.

**e** The main steps needed to make copper chloride crystals are listed below. Write ✎ numbers in the boxes to put them into a logical order.

Copper carbonate or copper oxide can be used to produce a copper salt.

Heat to evaporate off the excess water and concentrate the salt solution.  ☐

Mix the reactants and gently warm to speed up the reaction.  ☐

Filter off the excess unreacted copper oxide from the salt solution.  ☐

Remove crystals and dry.  ☐

Measure out the reactants.  ☐

Leave to crystallise.  ☐

Word and/ or symbol equations can be used to show your understanding of how to make a salt.

**2** Now answer ✎ the question yourself on paper. Use this checklist to review your answer.

| Checklist - have you: | ✓ |
|---|---|
| done what the command word has asked? | |
| organised your ideas logically? | |
| checked that someone could do the experiment from your instructions? | |

# Need more practice?

Exam questions may ask about different parts of one topic, or parts of more than one topic. Extended response questions could occur as questions about any topic, or questions about an experiment or investigation.

Have a go at these exam-style questions. Write ✏️ your answer to **2** on paper.

**Exam-style questions**

1  Explain the differences in properties of diamond and graphite.          **(6 marks)**

..........................................................................................

..........................................................................................

..........................................................................................

..........................................................................................

..........................................................................................

..........................................................................................

..........................................................................................

..........................................................................................

..........................................................................................

..........................................................................................

..........................................................................................

..........................................................................................

..........................................................................................

..........................................................................................

..........................................................................................

..........................................................................................

2  Describe a plan to determine the effect of temperature on the reaction between copper carbonate and dilute hydrochloric acid.

**(6 marks)**

**Boost your grade**

Make sure you are familiar with all the command words. Try changing the command word of different questions and see how that changes the answer you need to give. Practise choosing which information is relevant to the question rather than just writing all you know about a topic. This will help you to be more ordered with your response.

How confident do you feel about each of these **skills**? Colour in ✏️ the bars.

**1** How do I know what the question is asking me to do?

**2** How do I plan my answer?

**3** How do I choose the right detail to answer the question concisely?

# Answers

## Unit 1

### Page 2

① $C_3H_8 + 5O_2 \rightarrow 3CO_2 + 4H_2O$

②

| Particle | | Number of moles |
|---|---|---|
| H atoms | | 1 |
| $Ca^{2+}$ ions | | 2 |
| $OH^-$ ions | | 3 |
| O atoms | | 4 |

③ 7 mol of atoms (1 N atom, 5 H atoms, 1 O atom), 1 mol of $NH_4^+$ ion, 1 mol of $OH^-$ ion

④ 1; 2; 1

### Page 3

① 7

② atomic; $A_r$; periodic; relative formula mass; $A_r$

③ 32 + 16 + 16 = 64; 64 g

④

| Substance | Particle type | Formula | Relative particle mass | Mass of 1 mol (g) |
|---|---|---|---|---|
| Sodium chloride | ions | NaCl | 23 + 35.5 = 58.5 | 58.5 |
| Magnesium chloride | ions | $MgCl_2$ | 24 + 35.5 + 35.5 = 95 | 95 |
| Water | molecule | $H_2O$ | (2 x 1) + 16 = 18 | 18 |
| Glucose | molecule | $C_6H_{12}O_6$ | (6 × 12) + (12 × 1) + (6 × 16) = 180 | 180 |
| Sulfate | ion | $SO_4{}^{2-}$ | 32 + (4 × 16) = 96 | 96 |
| Calcium nitrate | ions | $Ca(NO_3)_2$ | 40 + (14 + 16 + 16 + 16)2 = 164 | 164 |

### Page 4

① a) 185.25 g

b) 1 Cu atom, 1 C atom, 3 O atoms so $M_r$ = 63.5 + 12 + (3 × 16) = 123.5

c) $\frac{185.25}{123.5}$ = 1.5 mol

② a) 213 g; 71    b) $\frac{213}{71}$; 3 mol

③ 3 mol × 6.02 × $10^{23}$ = 1.806 × $10^{24}$ = 1.81 × $10^{24}$ molecules (3 sf)

④ mass = number of moles × $M_r$ = 0.06 × 17 = 1.02 g

### Page 5

① a) 224 g    b) 16

c)

| | Iron (Fe) | Oxygen (O) |
|---|---|---|
| Mass (g) | 224 | 96 |
| Relative atomic mass, $A_r$ | 56 | 16 |
| $\frac{mass}{A_r}$ = number of moles | $\frac{224}{56}$ = 4 | $\frac{96}{16}$ = 6 |
| Find the simplest ratio of the number of moles by dividing by the smallest number | $\frac{4}{4}$ = 1 | $\frac{6}{4}$ = 1.5 |
| If needed, multiply by 2 to make the simplest ratio as whole numbers | 2 | 3 |
| Ratio of atoms | 2 iron atoms for every 3 oxygen atoms | |
| Empirical formula | $Fe_2O_3$ | |

② a) 5.4 g and 21.3 g    b) In the periodic table

c)

| | Aluminium (Al) | Chlorine (Cl) |
|---|---|---|
| Mass (g) | 5.4 | 21.3 |
| Relative atomic mass, $A_r$ | 27 | 35.5 |
| $\frac{mass}{A_r}$ = number of moles | $\frac{5.4}{27}$ = 0.2 | $\frac{21.3}{35.5}$ = 0.6 |
| Find the simplest ratio of the number of moles by dividing by the smallest number | $\frac{0.2}{0.2}$ = 1 | $\frac{0.6}{0.2}$ = 3 |
| Ratio of atoms | 1 aluminium atom for every 3 chlorine atoms | |
| Empirical formula | $AlCl_3$ | |

### Page 6

① a) highlighted: 12, formula, 69, mol

b) circled: 23, 16 , 51, 51, 1.3529, 1.4

c) $M_r$ = (2 × 23) + 12 + (3 × 16) = 106; $\frac{69}{106}$ = 0.65 mol

② a) First row: masses of lead and bromine have been swapped in error. $M_r$ of lead stated as 270 when it is 207. Results of calculations are incorrect, as is empirical formula.

b)

| Lead (Pb) | Bromine (Br) |
|---|---|
| $\frac{41.4}{207}$ = 0.2 | $\frac{32}{80}$ = 0.4 |
| $\frac{0.2}{0.2}$ = 1 | $\frac{0.4}{0.2}$ = 2 |
| Empirical formula is $PbBr_2$ | |

### Page 7

Exam-style question

1 (a) $M_r$ of $CaCO_3$ = 40 + 12 + (3 × 16) = 100 (1)

or 100 g = 1 mol; number of moles = $\frac{286}{100}$

= 2.86 mol (1)

(b) number of molecules = 5 × 6.02 × $10^{23}$ = 3.01 × $10^{24}$ molecules (1)

(c)

| | Ca | O | |
|---|---|---|---|
| No. of moles | $\frac{50}{40} = 1.25$ | $\frac{20}{16} = 1.25$ | (1) |
| Ratio | 1 | 1 | (1) |
| Empirical formula | CaO | | (1) |

Empirical formula = CaO

## Page 8

### Exam-style questions

1   $M_r = (2 \times 7) + 32 + (16 \times 4) = 110$ (1)

Number of moles of lithium sulfate $= \frac{282}{110}$
$= 2.56\,mol$ (1)

Number of moles of Li ions $= 5.12\,mol$ (1)

2   $0.5 \times 6.02 \times 10^{23} = 3.01 \times 10^{23}$ (1)

3

| C | H | Cl | |
|---|---|---|---|
| $\frac{360}{12} = 30$ | $\frac{60}{1} = 60$ | $\frac{1065}{35.5} = 30$ | (1) |
| $\frac{30}{30} = 1$ | $\frac{60}{30} = 2$ | $\frac{30}{30} = 1$ | (1) |
| Empirical formula is $CH_2Cl$ | | | (1) |

# Unit 2

## Page 10

① B mass of solute (g) = concentration (g dm$^{-3}$) × volume of solution (dm$^3$)

C volume of solution (dm$^3$) $= \frac{\text{mass of solute (g)}}{\text{concentration (g dm}^{-3})}$

② $A_r$ or $M_r = \frac{\text{mass of substance (g)}}{\text{number of moles}}$

③ number of moles $= 0.6 = \frac{\text{mass}}{23}$

$0.6 \times 23 = \left(\frac{\text{mass}}{23}\right) \times 23$

mass $= 13.8\,g$

## Page 11

① 5, 4, 1, 3, 6, 2

② 
1   0.03 highlighted
2   mass = number of moles × $M_r$
3   $12 + (4 \times 1) = 16$
4   $0.03 \times 16$    5   $0.48\,g$

③ 
1   0.31 kg highlighted
2   number of moles $= \frac{\text{mass (g)}}{M_r}$
3   a   $(2 \times 23) + 16 = 62$
    b   $0.31\,kg = 310\,g$
4   $\frac{310\,g}{62}$    5   $5.0\,mol$

## Page 12

① 
a   Highlighted as follows: 0.0801, 24.9
b   Highlighted as follows: 0.0801, 24.9
c   37.4 has 3 significant figures: 3, 7 and 4
d   If you write 37.4 to 1 significant figure, then the first sf is 3. The next digit is 7, so you round 3 up to 4. You need to write a zero to keep the place value. So, 37.4 to 1sf is 40.

If you write 37.4 to 2 sf, then the second sf is 7. The next digit is 4, so do not round up. 37.4 to 2 sf is 37.

② 
a   3    b   2    c   4
d   2    e   1    f   3

③ 

| Number | To 1 sf | To 2 sf | To 3 sf |
|---|---|---|---|
| 0.02564 | 0.03 | 0.026 | 0.0256 |
| 0.000 839 21 | 0.0008 | 0.000 84 | 0.000 839 |
| 1.035 | 1 | 1.0 | 1.04 |
| 609.72 | 600 | 610 | 610 |

## Page 13

① 
a   $CuSO_4$; $MgSO_4$
b   $63.5 + 32 + (4 \times 16) = 159.5$
c   $\frac{319}{159.5}$; 2 mol
d   $24 + 32 + (4 \times 16) = 120$
e   1; 1    f   2 mol
g   $2 \times 120 = 240\,g$ (2 sf)

② 

| Substance | $CuSO_4$ | $MgSO_4$ |
|---|---|---|
| Mass in g | 319 | 240 |
| $M_r$ | 159.5 | 120 |
| Mole ratio | 1 | 1 |
| Number of moles | 2 | 2 |

## Page 14

① mass = moles × $M_r$

$M_r$ of $Pb(NO_3)_2 = 207 + 2 \times (14 + (3 \times 16))$
$= 207 + (2 \times 62) = 331$

mass $= 1.68 \times 331$ (1)
$= 556\,g$ (3 sf) (1)

## Page 15

### Exam-style question

1   (a)   $M_r$ $H_2SO_4 = (2 \times 1) + 32 + (4 \times 16) = 98$

(b)   $M_r$ $NH_3 = 14 + (3 \times 1) = 17$

number of moles of $NH_3 = \frac{\text{mass}}{M_r} = \frac{3.4}{17} = 0.2\,mol$ (1)

From the balanced equation, 2 mol $NH_3$ produces 1 mol $(NH_4)_2SO_4$, so the mole ratio is 2 : 1.

0.2 mol $NH_3$ produces $\frac{0.2}{2} = 0.1\,mol\ (NH_4)_2SO_4$

mass of $(NH_4)_2SO_4$ produced = moles × $M_r$

$M_r\ (NH_4)_2SO_4 = (2 \times 14) + (2 \times 4 \times 1) + 32 + (4 \times 16) = 132$ (1)

mass $= 0.1 \times 132 = 13.2\,g = 13\,g$ (2 sf) (1)

## Page 16

### Exam-style question

1   $M_r$ $CaCO_3 = 40 + 12 + (3 \times 16) = 100$

Number of moles of $CaCO_3 = \frac{115}{100} = 1.15\,mol$

From the balanced equation, the mole ratio is 1 : 1, so 1.15 mol $CaCO_3$ produces 1.15 mol $Ca(NO_3)_2$

$M_r$ $Ca(NO_3)_2 = 40 + (2 \times 14) + (2 \times 3 \times 16) = 164$

mass = moles × $M_r = 1.15 \times 164 = 188.6\,g = 189\,g$ (3 sf)

# Unit 3

## Page 18

① Exothermic: Displacement reactions; Neutralisation reactions; Burning fuels

② Reaction 1: 5

Reaction 2: −3; endothermic

Reaction 3: −15; endothermic

③ collide; minimum; activation; faster; activation

④ 
- a gain
- b higher
- c faster
- d more collisions every second

⑤ Increasing temperature means the particles gain energy and move faster. There will be more collisions with the activation energy every second. So the rate of reaction increases.

## Page 19

① B In reaction **B** the relative heat energy of the reactants is less than that of the products.

C In reaction **A**, heat energy is given out to the surroundings.

E Reaction **A** is exothermic.

② a

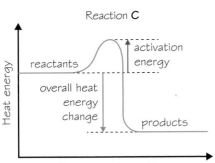

b given out; less

③ more; faster

## Page 20

① a B Temperature change data; E Bond energy data

b c d

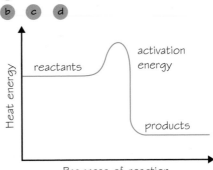

② a endothermic; decreased; less

b

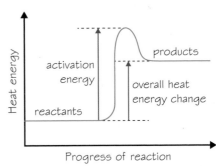

## Page 21

① endothermic; exothermic; bond; exothermic

② a 2; 2; single bond between H and Cl

b **Step 1:**

$1 \times$ H–H = 436 kJ mol$^{-1}$

$1 \times$ Cl–Cl = 242 kJ mol$^{-1}$

Total energy in = 678 kJ mol$^{-1}$

**Step 2:**

$2 \times$ H–Cl = $2 \times$ 431 kJ mol$^{-1}$

Total energy out = 862 kJ mol$^{-1}$

**Step 3:**

Energy change = energy in − energy out

= 678 − 862 = −184 kJ mol$^{-1}$

c It shows that the energy out is greater than the energy in.

d Exothermic

## Page 22

① 1: 2 H–H bonds are broken but only one was used in the calculation.

2: 4 O–H bonds are made but only two were used in the calculation.

② By being more specific and saying more energy is given out when making bonds in water than is taken in when breaking bonds in hydrogen and oxygen.

## Page 23

**Exam-style question**

1 (a) The relative amount of heat energy stored in the products is less than that stored in the reactants **(1)**. Therefore energy is given out to the surroundings **(1)**, making the reaction exothermic.

(b)

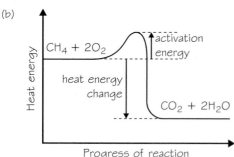

(c)  Calculate energy needed to break bonds **(1)**

Bonds broken = 4 × (C–H) + 2 × (O=O)

Energy in = (4 × 413) + 2 × (O=O)

= 1652 + 2 × (O=O) kJ mol$^{-1}$

Calculate energy released in forming bonds **(1)**

Bonds made = 2 × (C=O) + 4 × (O–H)

Energy out = (2 × 805) + (4 × 464)

= 1610 + 1856 = 3466 kJ mol$^{-1}$

Calculate energy change **(1)**

Energy change = energy in − energy out

−818 = 1652 + 2 × (O=O) − 3466

−818 − 1652 + 3466 = 2 × (O=O)

Evaluation of final answer **(1)**

2 × (O=O) = 996 kJ mol$^{-1}$

$O=O = \dfrac{996}{2} = 498$ kJ mol$^{-1}$

or

Energy in = 1652 + 2x

Energy out = 3466

Energy change = energy in − energy out

−818 = 1652 + 2x −3466

−818 = −1814 + 2x

Add 1814 to both sides

−818 + 1814 = 2x

996 = 2x

Divide both sides by 2

498 = x

## Page 24

**Exam-style questions**

1  (a)  The activation energy has not yet been reached **(1)** so the particles do not have enough energy for a successful collision to take place **(1)**.

  (b)  The reaction is exothermic **(1)** because the energy given out when the new bonds in the products are made is greater than the energy needed to break the bonds in the reactants **(1)**.

2  (a)  At the start of the reaction, the energy level increases to a maximum and then decreases rapidly **(1)**. The final energy level is lower than at the start of the reaction **(1)**.

  (b)  Calculate energy needed to break bonds **(1)**

Bonds broken = 1 × (N≡N) + 3 × (H–H)

Energy in = 945 + (3 × 436) = 2253 kJ mol$^{-1}$

Calculate energy released in forming bonds **(1)**

Bonds made = 6 × (N–H)

Energy out = (6 × 391) = 2346 kJ mol$^{-1}$

Calculate energy change **(1)**

Energy change = energy in − energy out

2253 − 2346 =

Evaluation of final answer **(1)**

−93 kJ mol$^{-1}$

# Unit 4

## Page 26

①  ⓐ  ammonium chloride
→ hydrogen chloride + ammonia

  ⓑ  ammonium chloride

  ⓒ  hydrogen chloride; ammonia

  ⓓ  hydrogen chloride; ammonia

  ⓔ  ammonium chloride

  ⓕ  the same

②  A conical flask with a tight-fitting bung.
A bottle with a screw top.

③  A: b, e; B: a, c

④  ⓐ  C        ⓑ  B

## Page 27

①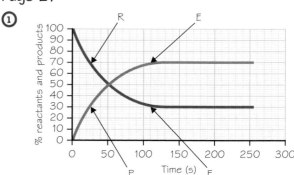

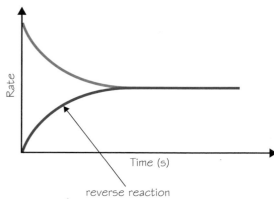

②  remains the same; equal to

## Page 28

①  ⓐ  forward reaction = exothermic;
reverse reaction = endothermic

  ⓑ  2nd row: Decreases       3rd row: Increases

  ⓒ  exothermic; Increasing

②  1st row: Moves to the left

2nd row: Decrease; The reverse reaction is endothermic and the reaction changes to increase the temperature.

## Page 29

①  ⓐ  Produce more ● and equilibrium position moves right.

  ⓑ  Produce more ● + ○ and position of equilibrium moves left.

②  position of equilibrium; fewest/smallest; four; two; right; ammonia/NH$_3$

## Page 30

(1) (a) B has specified the actual reactions with equal rates. The rate of the forward reaction is equal to the rate of the reverse reaction. A hasn't said this.

(b) B has correctly stated the required conditions but A has not mentioned that there must be a closed system.

(2) Both C and D got a mark for 'endothermic' but D did not get the reason right and C did.

## Page 31

### Exam-style question

1 (a) When the forwards and backwards reactions in a reversible chemical reaction are occurring at the same rate (1) in a closed system. (1)

(b) The brown colour becomes paler. (1) There are fewer molecules on the left so the position of equilibrium moves to the left to produce more colourless $N_2O_4$ and reduce the pressure. (1)

(c) More $NO_2$ is produced (1) as the position of equilibrium moves to the right (1) because the forward reaction is endothermic. (1)

## Page 32

### Exam-style questions

1 (a) They are the same (1) because the system is at dynamic equilibrium (1).

(b) The equilibrium is lost (1) because gas escapes from an open system (1).

2 (a) Three molecules of gas are reduced to two molecules of gas during the forward reaction. (1) Increasing the pressure favours the forward reaction. (1)

(b) The forward reaction is exothermic and favours lower temperatures. (1) At higher temperatures, less $SO_3$ would be produced/the reverse reaction is favoured. (1)

# Unit 5

## Page 34

(1) (a)

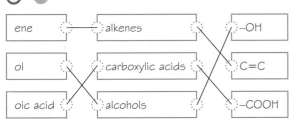

(b) alkenes, -oic acid, carboxylic acids

(c)

| Compound | Homologous series | Functional group |
|---|---|---|
| prop(ene) | alkene | C=C |
| ethan(oic acid) | carboxylic acid | -COOH |
| propan(ol) | alcohol | -OH |
| but(ene) | alkene | C=C |

(2) 3, 2, –oic acid, carboxylic acids, 4, –ene, alkenes

## Page 35

(1) (a)

A

B

C

| | Number of carbon atoms present | Prefix | Functional group present | Suffix | Name |
|---|---|---|---|---|---|
| A | 4 | but | C=C | ene | butene |
| B | 2 | eth | -OH | ol | ethanol |
| C | 4 | but | -COOH | oic acid | butanoic acid |

(2) (a) but

(b) 4

(c) ol

(d) -OH

(e) (g)

## Page 36

(1)

| Propane | Propene |
|---|---|
| contains single C-C bonds only | contains a C=C bond |
| saturated | unsaturated |
| does not undergo addition reactions | undergoes addition reactions |

(2)

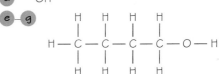

alkene    molecule reacting    product

③

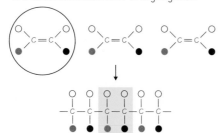

## Page 37

① **a** one of the molecules with a double bond circled

**b** Alternate atoms coloured red and black on the lower side of the product

**c** Any group of 2 C atoms with 2 white, a red and a black atom attached is highlighted

**d** It shows that there is a large number of repeating units in the polymer chain.

② **a** breaks open, ethene molecule, chain

**b**

③

| Name of polymer | Monomer | Repeating unit |
|---|---|---|
| Poly(propene) | Propene | |
| Poly (chloro-ethene) | Chloroethene | |

## Page 38

① **a** the functional group in both is OH

**b** ol

**c** COOH

**d** oic acid

**e** yes

**f** 3

**g** prop

**h** no

**i** yes

② propene: error 1 – the second carbon has 5 bonds as it has one extra hydrogen

propanoic acid: error 1 – there are 4 carbons present but there should be only 3

error 2 – the bond C–O should be C=O

butanol: error 1 – the structure should show all the bonds so the bond between O and H should be shown

## Page 39

### Exam-style questions

1 (a) $C=C$ structure with H, H on left and H, H on right **(1)**

(b) One of the bonds between the two carbon atoms opens up and joins to the ethene molecules on either side. **(2)**

2 (a) There are 3 carbons so the prefix is prop. It contains the –OH functional group so it is an alcohol.
propanol **(1)**

(b) structure H–C–C–C–(O–H) with O–H circled, labelled X **(1)**

3 (a) $C=C$ with –C–H structure, double bond circled

(b) structure with Br Br H H **(1)**

structure with H Br Br H **(1)**

(c) Add a few drops of bromine water to each sample and shake. If the bromine water stays brown then butane is present. If it goes colourless then butene is present.

## Page 40

### Exam-style questions

1 (a) H–C–C–C–C–C–H with Br Br H H H **(1)**

(b) dibromopropane **(1)**

**78** **Answers**

**2** (a)

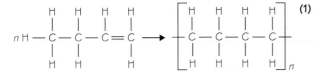

(1)

(b)  poly(butene) **(1)**

**3**  (1)

$$H - \underset{\underset{H}{|}}{\overset{\overset{H}{|}}{C}} - \underset{\underset{O-H}{|}}{\overset{\overset{\phantom{H}}{}}{C}} = O$$

# Unit 6

## Page 42

**①**

| Ion name | Ion formula | Cation | Anion |
|---|---|---|---|
| calcium | $Ca^{2+}$ | ✔ | |
| sulfate | $SO_4^{2-}$ | | ✔ |
| hydroxide | $OH^-$ | | ✔ |
| carbonate | $CO_3^{2-}$ | | ✔ |
| sodium | $Na^+$ | ✔ | |
| chloride | $Cl^-$ | | ✔ |

**②** ⓐ

| Compound name | Compound formula | Name and formula of the cation present | Name and formula of the anion present |
|---|---|---|---|
| calcium sulfate | $CaSO_4$ | calcium $Ca^{2+}$ | sulfate $SO_4^{2-}$ |
| potassium chloride | $KCl$ | potassium $K^+$ | chloride $Cl^-$ |
| copper carbonate | $CuCO_3$ | copper $Cu^{2+}$ | carbonate $CO_3^{2-}$ |
| lithium iodide | $LiI$ | lithium $Li^+$ | iodide $I^-$ |

ⓑ  Correct sentence is:

Copper chloride contains **negative** chloride ions and a **positive** copper ion. The formula of copper chloride is $CuCl_2$.

**③** ⓐ

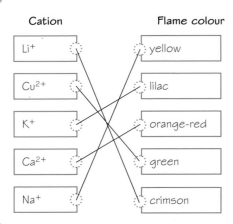

ⓑ  D A C B

## Page 43

**①**  potassium $K^+$

**②** ⓐ  copper hydroxide

ⓑ  circle copper hydroxide in ⓐ

ⓒ  The copper(II) hydroxide formed is insoluble.

**③**  sulfate, sodium hydroxide, green, brown

**④** ⓐ  $Fe^{2+}$ (aq) + $2OH^-$ (aq) → $Fe(OH)_2$(s)

$Fe^{3+}$ (aq) + $3OH^-$ (aq) → $Fe(OH)_3$(s)

## Page 44

**①** ⓐ  colourless, milky

ⓑ  silver carbonate, barium carbonate, precipitate, dilute acid

**②** ⓐ  $SO_4^{2-}$, (aq), $BaSO_4$, (s)

ⓑ  nitrate $NO_3^-$, sulfate $SO_4^{2-}$

ⓒ  There are sulfate ions present in sulfuric acid which would react with the barium ions. These cause a white precipitate and interfere with the test.

**③**  To remove carbonate ions, which would form a white precipitate and so cause a false positive result.

There are chloride ions present in hydrochloric acid which would react with the silver ions. These cause a white precipitate and interfere with the test.

## Page 45

**①** ⓐ  circle bromide, chloride

ⓑ  anions

ⓒ  silver nitrate

ⓓ  nitric acid, silver nitrate, white, cream

**②** ⓐ  sulfate, chloride

ⓑ  anions

ⓒ  add dilute nitric acid followed by silver nitrate add dilute hydrochloric acid followed by barium chloride

ⓓ  1 white precipitate for potassium chloride
2 white precipitate for potassium sulfate

**③** ⓐ  calcium, aluminium

ⓑ  cations

ⓒ  Adding sodium hydroxide solution in excess will identify the two substances

## Page 46

**①** ⓐ  Other metal ion solutions, such as calcium and magnesium, also give white precipitates when sodium hydroxide is added.

ⓑ  aluminium hydroxide

ⓒ  $Al^{3+}$(aq) + $3OH^-$(aq) → $Al(OH)_3$(aq)

**②** ⓐ  To remove carbonate ions which would give a false positive test.

ⓑ  Silver chloride is formed, which is insoluble.

ⓒ  $Ag^+$(aq) + $Cl^-$(aq) → $AgCl$(s)

## Page 47

Exam-style question

1    (a)

| Test | Aluminium chloride solution | Calcium carbonate solution | Iron(II) sulfate solution |
|---|---|---|---|
| Adding dilute nitric acid followed by silver nitrate | white precipitate **(1)** | no change | no change |
| Adding dilute hydrochloric acid followed by barium chloride | no change **(1)** | no change **(1)** | white ppt |

   (b)   To remove carbonate ions which would form a precipitate. **(1)**

   (c)   $Ba^{2+}(aq)$ **(1)** $+ SO_4{}^{2-}(aq)$ **(1)** $\rightarrow BaSO_4(s)$ **(1)**

   (d)

| | Aluminium chloride | Calcium carbonate | Iron(II) sulfate |
|---|---|---|---|
| flame test | no colour | orange-red **(1)** | no colour |
| adding sodium hydroxide solution | white precipitate **(1)** | white precipitate **(1)** | green precipitate **(1)** |
| adding excess sodium hydroxide solution | no change **(1)** | no change **(1)** | no change |

## Page 48

Exam-style questions

1    A    potassium iodide **(1)**

     B    sodium sulfate **(1)**

     C    iron(III) chloride **(1)**

2    Flame colour for lithium is red and calcium is orange-red. This makes it hard to distinguish between the two colours. Each metal ion produces its own individual spectrum which can then be compared to known Li and Ca spectra. Therefore, the results from the flame photometer are more likely to be correct.

3    Dissolve a spatula of each solid in water.

     To each solution, add a few drops of sodium hydroxide solution; both should give a white precipitate. Add excess sodium hydroxide solution and the aluminium hydroxide precipitate will dissolve to give a colourless solution.

     To fresh samples of each solution, add a few drops of nitric acid followed by silver nitrate solution. If it is a chloride a white precipitate will form, if it is a bromide a cream precipitate will form and if it is an iodide a yellow precipitate will form.

# Unit 7

## Page 50

(1)   (a)   acid + alkali → salt + water

      (b)

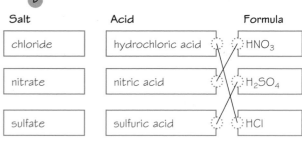

| Salt | Acid | Formula |
|---|---|---|
| chloride | hydrochloric acid | $HNO_3$ |
| nitrate | nitric acid | $H_2SO_4$ |
| sulfate | sulfuric acid | HCl |

      (c)   sodium hydroxide + hydrochloric acid → sodium chloride + water

            potassium hydroxide + sulfuric acid → potassium sulfate + water

            nitric acid + calcium hydroxide → calcium nitrate + water

(2)   (a)   labels, from top to bottom:

            burette

            pipette (safety) filler

            pipette

            white tile

            conical flask

      (b)   **B** To help you to see the colour change of the indicator more easily.

## Page 51

(1)   curved, bottom, eye, 22.1

(2)   Steps 4, 1, 2, 3

(3)   (a)   The experiment is repeated for reliability. Reliability means that similar results, with little variation, are obtained when the experiment is repeated.

      (b)   The flask must be swirled to ensure the reactants are mixed thoroughly and thus react fully.

(4)   conical flask, pipette, white tile, sodium hydroxide, burette, changed colour

## Page 52

(1)   (a)   circled 12.50 12.45 12.40

      (b)   It is less accurate. Unlike in the following titrations, the student does not have an idea of an approximate end point and may add the solution too quickly, overshooting the end point and leading to a larger volume.

(2)   (a)   25.40, 25.45

      (b)   25.40, 25.40, 25.45

      (c)   $\dfrac{25.40 + 25.40 + 25.45}{3} = 25.42 \text{ cm}^3$

      (d)   yellow to red

(3)   A B C D

## Page 53

(1)   (a)   19.60 cm³, concentration

      (b)   0.400

② 1, 0.01568

③ $1000 \times \dfrac{0.01568}{25.0} = 0.6272$; to 3 sf, this is 0.627

## Page 54

① **a** Using a pipette and safety pipette filler

**b** That there are no air bubbles and the tap is filled

**c** To the bottom of the meniscus at eye level

**d** Added in drops with swirling.

② **a** the volume of KOH is 22.50 cm³ not 25.0

**b** moles $= \dfrac{22.50}{1000} \times 0.100 = 0.00225$

**c** 0.001125

**d** $\dfrac{1000 \times 0.001125}{25.0} = 0.045\,\text{mol dm}^{-3}$

## Page 55

Exam-style question

1 (a) pipette (accurate to 1 dp) **(1)**

(b) Add 3 drops of named indicator, e.g. phenolphthalein, methyl orange, litmus, to the conical flask **(1)**. Rinse and fill the burette with sodium hydroxide solution ensuring there are no air bubbles and the tap is filled. Place the conical flask on a white tile under the burette **(1)**. Add sodium hydroxide with swirling, and dropwise near the end point until the indicator changes colour **(1)**. Phenolphthalein, colourless to pink / methyl orange, red to yellow / litmus, red to blue. **(1)**

(c) 1 mark for selecting titration 2 and 3;

$\dfrac{26.20 + 26.10}{2} = 26.15\,\text{cm}^3$ **(1)**

(d) moles of NaOH $= \dfrac{\text{vol} \times \text{conc}}{1000} = \dfrac{26.15 \times 0.200}{1000}$

$= 0.00523$ **(1)**

ratio 2 moles NaOH : 1 mole $H_2SO_4$

$0.00523 : \dfrac{0.00523}{2} = 0.002615$ **(1)**

moles $H_2SO_4 \times \dfrac{1000}{\text{vol}} = $ concentration of $H_2SO_4$ (mol dm⁻³)

$\dfrac{0.002615 \times 1000}{25.0} = 0.1046\,\text{mol dm}^{-3}$ **(1)**

$= 0.105\,\text{mol dm}^{-3}$ to 3 sf **(1)**

## Page 56

Exam-style question

1 (a) phenolphthalein / methyl orange / litmus **(1)**

(b) Phenolphthalein, pink to colourless; methyl orange, yellow to orange/red; litmus, blue to red. **(1)**

(c) Fill the pipette with sodium hydroxide using a pipette filler **(1)**, transfer it to the conical flask and expel **(1)**.

(d) moles $H_2SO_4 = \dfrac{\text{volume (cm}^3)}{1000} \times$ concentration (mol dm⁻³)

$= \dfrac{22.50 \times 0.500}{1000} = 0.01125\,\text{mol}$ **(1)**

Mole ratio is 1 $H_2SO_4$ : 2 NaOH. There are twice the number of moles of NaOH as there are of $H_2SO_4$.

or

moles of NaOH $= 2 \times 0.01125 = 0.0225\,\text{mol}$ **(1)**

concentration NaOH $= \dfrac{\text{moles} \times 1000}{\text{volume (cm}^3)}$

$= \dfrac{0.0225 \times 1000}{25.0} = 0.9$ **(1)**

concentration $= 0.900\,\text{mol dm}^{-3}$ **(1)**

# Unit 8

## Page 58

①

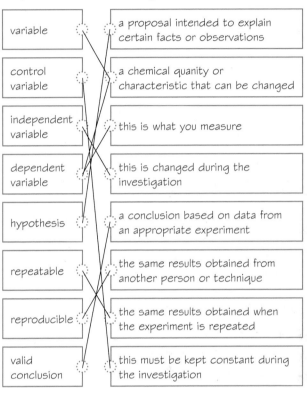

| Key word | Meaning |
|---|---|
| variable | a proposal intended to explain certain facts or observations |
| control variable | a chemical quanity or characteristic that can be changed |
| independent variable | this is what you measure |
| dependent variable | this is changed during the investigation |
| hypothesis | a conclusion based on data from an appropriate experiment |
| repeatable | the same results obtained from another person or technique |
| reproducible | the same results obtained when the experiment is repeated |
| valid conclusion | this must be kept constant during the investigation |

② **a** A catalysts; B acid concentration; C mobile phase

**b** A time; B temperature change; C position of spots

③ cannot; small; one data point; not possible

## Page 59

① **a** Increasing the current during the electrolysis will increase the mass of metal deposited on the negative electrode.

**b** A Make up a solution of copper sulfate or copper chloride solution to test. C In electrolysis, electricity is used to split up compounds, so we need to set up an electric circuit. D Ammeters are used to measure current. F Graphite electrodes are inert.

**c** first row: current

second row: mass of metal deposited at the negative electrode

third row: any two from: voltage / salt solution / concentration of the salt solution / graphite electrodes / time circuit switched on

## Page 60

**(1)** **(a)** i A  electric current; B  copper salt

ii A  mass of copper; B  products produced at the cathode

iii A  copper salt, type of electrode, concentration of salt solution

B  electric current, concentration of salt solution, type of electrode

iv The effect of changing the copper salt on the products produced at the cathode.

**(b)** 0.1–0.5 A

**(c)** 0.2 A and 1 A are not ranges. 0.1 A–0.5 A is big enough to show a pattern. The values of 0.01 and 0.02 are too close together.

## Page 61

**(1)** precise; accurate

**(2)** A; C; B; D

**(3)** **(a)** 0.63

**(b)** Maybe the current was not controlled properly and it went higher / perhaps they misread the number on the balance

**(c)** Each individual measurement / data point will have some errors in it. By taking the mean some of the errors will cancel out.

**(d)** reproducible; low; one decimal place

## Page 62

**(1)** **(a)** We don't really know because it is hard to see the pattern when there are no repeats. They could compare their results with those collected by student B.

**(b)** Repeat each experiment and take the mean.

**(c)** It is an anomalous result and did not fit with the other two data points which were exactly the same.

**(d)** The control variables may not be probably controlled or an error is made when either reading or recording the data point.

## Page 63

**Exam-style question**

1 (a) chlorine gas

(b) Place some damp litmus paper on / near the anode. **(1)** If it is bleached and goes white, chlorine gas is a product. **(1)**

(c) (i) $Cu^{2+} + 2e^- \rightarrow Cu$

(ii) mass of the cathode at the start and finish of each experiment **(1)**; the current **(1)**

(iii) Any two from: concentration of the copper chloride solution; the time the current is switched on; voltage during each experiment; the graphite electrodes

(iv) Repeat each experiment two / three times **(1)** and take the mean results **(1)**

## Page 64

**Exam-style questions**

1 Wear eye protection.

Mix the sodium carbonate solution and the zinc chloride solution in a beaker **(1)**, then filter the mixture **(1)**.

To make sure it is pure, rinse the beaker with a little distilled water and pour the distilled water over the precipitate in the funnel **(1)**.

Carefully remove the filter paper containing the precipitate and dry it in a warm oven **(1)**.

2 Sample answer:

potassium hydroxide + sulfuric acid → potassium sulfate + water

$$2KOH + H_2SO_4 \rightarrow K_2SO_4 + 2H_2O$$

Wearing safety glasses, fill a burette with dilute sulfuric acid ensuring the meniscus is at $0\,cm^3$. Measure out $25\,cm^3$ of potassium hydroxide solution into a conical flask using a pipette and pipette filler.

Add a few drops of an indicator (e.g. phenolphthalein is pink in alkaline solutions and turns colourless at the end point).

Add the acid slowly from the burette, swirling the conical flask to mix the acid and alkali thoroughly. Note the volume of acid required for the colour change.

Repeat the experiment but this time add the acid drop by drop near the end point to improve the accuracy.

To produce the salt crystals, repeat the experiment without the indicator, adding the exact volume of acid to the alkali.

Evaporate the water from the solution to produce potassium sulfate crystals.

# Unit 9

## Page 66

**(1)** Link your ideas together to show understanding.

Use correct scientific vocabulary.

Write your answer in an ordered way.

**(2)**

| Give two signs of a reaction that would be **seen** when a piece of sodium is dropped into a container of water. | The metal moves around on the water rapidly because the reaction is very vigorous. |
| --- | --- |
| | The metal moves around on the water rapidly. |
| Describe what would be **seen** when a piece of sodium is dropped into a container of water. | The metal disappears. |
| | Bubbles coming off where the sodium meets the water. |
| Explain what would be **seen** when a piece of sodium is dropped into a container of water. | Bubbles. |
| | Bubbles because hydrogen gas is given off. |

# Page 67

1.
   a. Describe
   b. Write down some key facts from the information provided.

2.
   a. relative; based on
   b. The word 'relative' is important because it is telling you that you must compare the reactivity of the different metals.

      'Based on' means you use the facts in the table.
   c. experimental data

3.
   a. What you see/observe when different metals react with different substances.
   b. Reaction with water column; reaction with hydrochloric acid column.
   c. copper; lithium; zinc; magnesium
   d. i  copper, zinc, magnesium, lithium

      ii  copper, zinc, magnesium, lithium
   e. Both copper and zinc do not react with water, but zinc does react with hydrochloric acid. This tells me that zinc is more reactive than copper.

# Page 68

1. Cross out:

   Consider the variables involved in the reaction. What needs to be changed or controlled?

   How will you make it a fair test?

   How will you record your results?

2. $CuO(s) + H_2SO_4(aq) \rightarrow CuSO_4 (aq) + H_2O (l)$

3.
   a. reactants, products and states
   b. What is the chemical reaction?

      What reactants will you need?

      What equipment will you use?

      What will you observe or measure?

# Page 69

1. When you explain something you must give a reason for your answer. Reasons are not required when you describe something.

2. Relative reactivity; halogens; electronic structure

3. The reactivity of halogens decreases down the group.

   The electronic structure is the way in which an atom's electrons are arranged.

   The electronic structure of chlorine is 2,8,7.

   As you go down the group the distance between the electron in the outer shell and the nucleus increases.

   The formation of negative ions is important for reactivity.

   The force of attraction depends on distance from the nucleus.

4. The relative reactivity of the halogens from most to least reactive: fluorine, chlorine, bromine, iodine.

# Page 70

1.
   a. Describe            b. 1st two sentences
   c. No                  d. No

   Sample answer:

2. Take 2 pieces of the same size of copper and place each into a test tube. Add 5 cm³ of zinc sulfate to one and 5 cm³ of magnesium sulfate to the other. Record any observations. Repeat the same process with pieces of zinc added to copper sulfate and magnesium sulfate solutions of the same concentration. Then repeat with pieces of magnesium added to copper sulfate and zinc sulfate.

| | Observations | | |
|---|---|---|---|
| | copper sulfate | zinc sulfate | magnesium sulfate |
| Copper | X | | |
| Zinc | | X | |
| Magnesium | | | X |

Record the observations in this table. If there is a reaction you may see a colour change, the metal disappearing and a new metal deposited. An increase in temperature could be measured as the reaction is exothermic.

The most reactive metal is the one that reacts with both sulfate solutions and the least reactive metal is the one that reacts with neither.

# Page 71

1.
   a. Describe
   b. eg Recall some facts, events or process in an accurate way. Statements need to be developed as they are often linked. You do not need to give reasons.
   c. hydrochloric acid
   d. A; C; B; D
   e. 1 Measure out the reactants; 2 Mix the reactants and gently warm to speed up the reaction; 3 Filter off the excess unreacted copper oxide from the salt solution; 4 Heat to evaporate off the excess water and concentrate the salt solution; 5 Leave to crystallise; 6 Remove crystals and dry

2. Answer could include the following points in a logical order for 6 marks:

   (Accept either equation as both will produce the same result.)

   copper oxide + hydrochloric acid
   → copper chloride + water

   $CuO(s) + 2HCl(aq) \rightarrow CuCl_2(aq) + H_2O(l)$

   or

   copper carbonate + hydrochloric acid
   → copper chloride + water + carbon dioxide

   $CuCO_3(s) + 2HCl(aq) \rightarrow CuCl_2(aq) + H_2O(l) + CO_2(g)$

   Wearing safety glasses, measure out some hydrochloric acid in a measuring cylinder and transfer it to a beaker. Add some copper oxide / copper carbonate to the acid and mix well. Heat gently until no more solid dissolves.

   Fold a piece of filter paper and place it in a filter funnel in the top of a conical flask or beaker. Filter the hot mixture through the funnel. Pour the filtrate into an evaporating basin and gently warm over a water bath until the volume has reduced by about half.

Remove the evaporating basin from the heat and leave the concentrated solution to cool and the copper chloride crystals to form. Finally dry the crystals by dabbing them on a piece of filter paper.

## Page 72

### Exam-style questions

1   Answer could include the following points in a logical order for 6 marks:

Diamond and graphite are allotropes of carbon. They are both covalent, giant molecular structures with very high melting points. This is because of the strong covalent bonds between the carbon atoms which need to be broken to change them from a solid to a liquid.

However, the structural arrangements of the carbon atoms are different, which explains the differences in their properties.

Diamond has a tetrahedral arrangement of carbon atoms which makes it very hard and rigid.

Graphite is softer than diamond because it has a layered structure. Each carbon atom is covalently bonded to three others forming layers containing hexagonal rings. There are weak intermolecular forces between the layers which allow them to slide over each other. There are also delocalised electrons which are free to move as they are not all held in the covalent bonds like diamond. This means that graphite conducts electricity whereas diamond doesn't.

2   Answer could include the following points in a logical order for 6 marks:

copper carbonate + hydrochloric acid
$\rightarrow$   copper chloride + water + carbon dioxide

As carbon dioxide is given off, the reaction can be followed by measuring the volume of gas produced using a gas syringe attached to the top of a conical flask.

Wear safety glasses throughout the experiment and wipe up any spillages immediately.

For each experiment use the same:

- mass of copper carbonate (2 g measured on a balance);
- volume of dilute hydrochloric acid (50 $cm^3$ measured in a measuring cylinder);
- time to collect the carbon dioxide gas (30 seconds measured using a stop watch).

Temperature is the only variable to be changed. This can be done using a large beaker containing five different temperatures of water to get a good range of results. Ice can be used to cool the water bath below room temperature. Different amounts of water from a boiled kettle can be used for the higher temperatures. (Take care with hot water.)

Put a conical flask containing 50 $cm^3$ dilute HCl into the water bath to give it time to warm up or cool down. Record the temperature of the acid. Add the copper carbonate and seal the gas syringe onto the top of the conical flask. Start timing and measure the volume of gas collected after 30 seconds.

Record the results in this table.

| Temperature of hydrochloric acid (°C) | Volume of gas produced in 30 seconds ($cm^3$) |
|---|---|
|  |  |
|  |  |
|  |  |
|  |  |
|  |  |

Ideally the whole experiment should be repeated to confirm the trend. A graph of volume of carbon dioxide produced ($cm^3$) against temperature can be drawn to show the effect of temperature on this reaction.